Controlled Test Atmospheres

Principles and Techniques

Controlled Test Atmospheres

Principles and Techniques

Gary O. Nelson

Lawrence Radiation Laboratory
University of California
Livermore

Second Printing, 1972

© Copyright 1971 by Ann Arbor Science Publishers, Inc.
P.O. Box 1425,
Ann Arbor, Michigan 48106

Library of Congress Catalog Card No. 73–141231
ISBN 250–97506–8
Printed in the United States of America

Foreword

If asked to name the areas of chemistry in which the greatest upsurge of interest occurred in recent years, one would have to list studies of gas phase systems, primarily because of the increased interest in our environment. Fundamental to any chemical research is the ability to perform accurate and reliable measurements of the characteristics of the system, to successfully generate standards, and to control the parameters of the study. To chemists with traditional experience and training, the path toward successful studies with gas phase systems is strewn with technical pitfalls.

The author has made an important contribution for researchers planning or doing work that involves controlled atmospheres. He has made a particularly thorough presentation of the field from the basic calculations to the most sophisticated techniques. Of particular note are the tables and appendices with their wealth of data and the extensive list of references. The book is a worthwhile acquisition for the convenience of these sources alone. Recommendations about the choice and use of apparatus should save workers a great deal of time and effort. Numerous solved problems represent the methods for most calculations.

Note — *All* the techniques described can be used for GC and IR spec. There is no one special section dealing with them. Analytical chemists will find these techniques useful in dealing with the preparation of standard gas mixtures for gas chromatography and for gas phase infrared spectroscopy and a unique source of reliable and practical information.

In summary, this book is a painstakingly thorough survey of the techniques of an important and expanding area of chemistry.

Ronald M. Scott
Professor of Chemistry
Eastern Michigan University

Ypsilanti, Michigan
April, 1971

Preface

The preparation of known gas mixtures has long been a major concern to those involved in analytical and experimental work. Many interesting and useful methods have been developed, but they are scattered throughout the literature and have never been collected and evaluated in a single publication.

This book provides a firm theoretical basis for using the available techniques and makes practical suggestions about the production of known test atmospheres. The systems discussed range from the simple, static, equipment used in the field to the more sophisticated dynamic apparatus used in the laboratory for air-pollution and animal-toxicology investigations. The book also describes methods of making precise mixtures for gas chromatography and gas-phase infrared spectroscopy.

This book will serve as a valuable guide not only for those who work with air pollution, analytical chemistry, and industrial hygiene, but also for anyone who simply wants to make standard multicomponent gas and vapor mixtures.

I am greatly indebted to a number of people who helped make this book possible. The Technical Information Department of the Lawrence Radiation Laboratory, Livermore, was particularly helpful, especially Wilma T. Leon, who drew the illustrations, and William T. Ryan, who assisted in document acquisition. I also want to thank Joe Lipera, Carl L. Lindeken, and Dr. Walter E. Ruch for their encouragement and guidance. A special note of thanks goes to Dr. Ralph G. Smith for manuscript review and to Doris E. Osinski for her deciphering and typing of the first draft. I would also like to thank the U.S. Atomic Energy Commission, under whose auspices this book was written.

Gary O. Nelson

Livermore, California, April 1971

Contents

Summary 195

Appendices

References 229

Chapter 1

Introduction and General Principles

INTRODUCTION

There is no one method of producing gas and vapor mixtures for experimental work. Each situation must be dealt with separately, and the system that is successful for one application must often be altered for other applications in order to accommodate different experimental criteria. Before a scientist devises any system, he must decide what concentrations, volumes, flow rates, accuracies, and equilibrium times are required, and he must determine if his material resources and his budget are sufficient to fabricate such a system. The summary on page 195 can be used as a guide to determine what system or systems are applicable to a particular experiment.

FUNDAMENTAL GAS LAWS

The production of standard gas mixtures requires a working knowledge of the behavior of gases in relation to temperature and pressure. One must also be able to convert flow rate, volume, and density measurements from one measurement system to another. Although gases and vapors usually act in a predictable manner, it is necessary to recognize deviations and to apply appropriate corrections.

The purpose of this chapter is to derive, organize, and correlate

1

the important fundamental relationships that exist in both pure and mixed gases. The mathematical expressions described in this chapter will appear throughout the remaining five chapters, and sample calculations will be given as each equation is used in its own specialized manner. The mathematical considerations discussed below are not rigorous, but they are sufficient to provide a sound basis for dealing with practical problems in a practical way.

Ideal Gases

Pressure, Temperature, and Volume

The relationship between the pressure and volume of a gas at a constant temperature is described by Boyle's law, which states that the volume, V, is inversely proportional to the pressure, P:

$$V^* = K\left(\frac{1}{P}\right), \tag{1}$$

where K is a proportionality constant, or

$$P_1 V_1 = P_2 V_2 . \tag{2}$$

The relationship between the temperature and volume of a gas at a constant pressure is described by Charles' law, which states that the volume is directly proportional to the absolute temperature, T:

$$V = KT . \tag{3}$$

A more general equation involving all three variables can be obtained by combining Equations 1 and 3:

$$PV = KT \tag{4}$$

or

$$\frac{P_1 V_1}{T_1} = \frac{P_2 V_2}{T_2} . \tag{5}$$

If K is proportional to the number of moles of gas, n, then

$$PV = nRT , \tag{6}$$

which is the well-known ideal gas law. The most commonly used values of the molar gas constant, R, are listed in Appendix C.

°All mathematical symbols in this book are defined in Appendix K.

Density

The calculation of gas density is important both for correcting flow rates and for determining how well gases conform to the ideal gas law. If W is the weight and M is the molecular weight, then

$$n = \frac{W}{M} .$$ (7)

Equation 6 then becomes

$$PV = \frac{WRT}{M}$$ (8)

or

$$\frac{W}{V} = \frac{PM}{RT} ,$$ (9)

where W/V is the ideal gas density. The calculated densities of some of the more common gases are given in Appendix E.

Concentration

The concentrations of gas and vapor mixtures are almost always expressed in units of per cent or parts per million by volume, although in some air-pollution, industrial-hygiene, and animal-toxicology work the most convenient unit may be weight per unit volume. For concentrations above 0.1%, the concentration, C, is usually expressed in per cent. This can be calculated for ideal gases by

$$C_{\%} = \frac{10^2 \, v_a}{v_a + v_b + \ldots + v_n} = \frac{10^2 \, p_a}{p_a + p_b + \ldots + p_n} ,$$ (10)

where $v_{a,b,\ldots,n}$ and $p_{a,b,\ldots,n}$ are the volumes and partial pressures of components a, b, . . . , n at a constant temperature. For concentrations below 0.1%, the concentration is usually expressed in parts per million by volume (*i.e.*, the number of parts by volume of trace gas in a million parts of gas mixture). This can be calculated for ideal gases by

$$C_{ppm} = \frac{10^6 \, v_a}{v_D + v_a} = \frac{10^6 \, p_a}{p_D + p_a} ,$$ (11)

where v_D and p_D are the volume and pressure of the diluent gas. The v_a and the p_a terms are usually neglected when dealing with concentrations below 5000 parts per million since their contribution to the total volume is usually insignificant. However, above 5000 parts per million, the contaminant gas becomes more dominant and its volume must be included in the total gas volume. Table I illustrates how the numerical value of the concentration is altered depending on whether or not the trace-gas volume is included in the denominator of Equation 11.

Table I. Concentration by volume of gas A in a mixture of gases

A and B.

Based on total volume of gases A and B $(v_D + v_a)$		Based on volume of gas B (v_D) only	
(%)	(ppm)	(%)	(ppm)
0.0001	1	0.0001000001	1.000001
0.001	10	0.00100001	10.0001
0.01	100	0.010001	100.01
0.1	1,000	0.1001	1,001
0.5	5,000	0.5025	5,025
1	10,000	1.010	10,100
10	100,000	11.11	111,100
20	200,000	25	250,000
50	500,000	100	1,000,000
100	1,000,000	—	—

Concentration can also be calculated when a known weight or volume of a liquid is vaporized in a known volume of a diluent gas. If the liquid has a weight W and a molecular weight M, and if it is evaporated at a pressure P and a temperature T, then the volume of vapor produced is given by

$$v_a = \frac{WRT}{MP} .$$ (12)

If v_a is diluted with v_D, then the resulting concentration on a volume per cent basis is determined by the equation

$$C_{\%} = \frac{10^2 \, v_a}{v_a + v_D} = \frac{10^2 \, \frac{WRT}{MP}}{\frac{WRT}{MP} + v_D} = \frac{10^2}{1 + \frac{v_D MP}{WRT}} \qquad (13)$$

Similarly, the concentration in parts per million by volume is determined by

$$C_{ppm} = \frac{10^6 \, v_a}{v_D} = \frac{10^6 \, \frac{WRT}{MP}}{v_D} . \qquad (14)$$

Usually, W is expressed in terms of the volume of liquid, v_L, and density, ρ_L. Equation 14 then becomes

$$C_{ppm} = \frac{10^6 \, v_L \rho_L RT}{v_D MP} . \qquad (15)$$

At room temperature (25°C) and pressure (760 mm Hg), this reduces to

$$C_{ppm} = \frac{24.5 \times 10^6 \, v_L \rho_L}{v_D M} . \qquad (16)$$

Concentration is sometimes expressed in units of weight per unit volume* when the concentration of aerosols such as metal fumes, mists, or dusts in air or some other supporting gas is being measured. Copper, lead, and iron fumes are prime examples. Such concentration is calculated by

$$C_{w/v} = \frac{W}{v_D} , \qquad (17)$$

which is related to concentration in parts per million by

$$C_{w/v} = \frac{10^{-6} \, C_{ppm} MP}{RT} \qquad (18)$$

and to vapor pressure by

$$C_{w/v} = \frac{p_a MP}{p_D RT} . \qquad (19)$$

---

*Weight per unit volume is usually given in units of milligrams per cubic meter.

Usually, however, P_D closely approximates P. Equation 19 therefore simplifies to

$$C_{w/v} = \frac{p_a M}{RT} .$$ (20)

Nonideal Gases

Atmospheric Pressure

Most gases adhere closely to the ideal gas law at room temperature and atmospheric pressure. However, for the best accuracy with mixed gases, deviations from ideality must be taken into account, especially at high pressures. This is accomplished by comparing the actual gas density, ρ_A, with the ideal density, ρ_I, under the same conditions. The actual gas volume, v_A, can then be corrected to the ideal volume, v_I, and can be used to make precise gas mixtures by the equation

$$v_I = Kv_A = \frac{\rho_A}{\rho_I} v_A .$$ (21)

At 0° C and 760 mm Hg, ρ_I can be found from

$$\rho_I = \frac{M}{22.414} .$$ (22)

Values for ρ_A, ρ_I, and ρ_A/ρ_I under standard conditions are tabulated in Appendix E for easy reference.

High Pressure

If pressurized systems are used, the deviation from ideality becomes more pronounced and large correction factors must be applied if even moderate accuracies (± 10–20%) are to be achieved (see Figure 1). The correction factor, which is compressibility, κ, is defined by

$$\kappa = \frac{PV}{RT} ,$$ (23)

where P, V, and T are measured under the conditions of interest. Equation 10 then becomes

$$C_{\%} = \frac{10^2 \, \dfrac{p_a}{\kappa_a}}{\dfrac{p_a}{\kappa_a} + \dfrac{p_b}{\kappa_b} + \cdots + \dfrac{p_n}{\kappa_n}} \cdot \qquad (24)$$

The values of κ are known for pure gases, but not always for mixed gases.

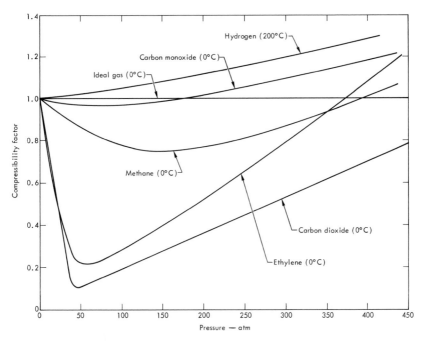

Figure 1. Compressibility versus pressure for six gases. Note the large deviations at 50 atm for ethylene and carbon dioxide.

Chapter 2

Air Purification

Laboratory compressed air is the most common source of diluent gas for low-concentration, high-volume standard gas mixtures. It is continuously supplied as needed, usually by diesel or electric compressors at pressures of 80 to 125 psi, and it is stored in holding tanks. Several undesirable contaminants can be introduced during compression and storage. Oil mists are a common by-product, as are substantial amounts of carbon dioxide, nitrogen dioxide, aldehydes, carbon monoxide, and unburned hydrocarbons. Acid gases as well as dust particles and pipe scales of all sizes are also a problem. Even if the air is known to be 99.9% pure, it can still contain up to 1000 ppm of undesirable materials. Before any quality low-concentration work can be done, the air-supply system must be scrupulously cleaned to prevent contamination and possible chemical reactions. The composition of clean, dry air is given in Table II.

This chapter describes the basic methods of removing contaminants from flowing air streams. General multipurpose filtering devices are discussed, as are methods for removing excess water vapor, oil mists, extraneous gases, and particulate matter. The air-purification procedures that are described can also be applied to such relatively stable gases as nitrogen and oxygen as well as to inert gases.

9

Table II.   Composition of clean,

dry air.

Nitrogen	78.08%
Oxygen	20.95%
Argon	0.934%
Carbon dioxide	0.033%
Neon	18.2 ppm
Helium	5.24 ppm
Methane	2.0 ppm
Krypton	1.14 ppm
Hydrogen	0.5 ppm
Nitrous oxide	0.5 ppm
Xenon	0.087 ppm

REMOVAL OF WATER VAPOR

Moisture can be removed from gases by a variety of methods. Chief among these are adsorption, absorption, cooling, compression, and combined compression and cooling. Usually, only the first three methods are used in the laboratory.

Solid Dessicants

Solid desiccants constitute the most conventional method of removing water vapor in the laboratory. They remove moisture either by chemical reaction (absorption) or by capillary condensation (adsorption).[1] Solid absorbing agents include calcium chloride, calcium sulfate, and magnesium perchlorate; solid adsorbing agents include activated alumina and silica gel. Solid desiccants are one of the most practical tools for drying gases because they are commercially available, they are easy to store, they can be regenerated by heating, and they often indicate their condition by their color.

Solid desiccants are generally evaluated by comparing their drying efficiencies and capacities. The efficiencies of drying agents (*i.e.*, the degree of dryness achieved) can be compared by measuring the water vapor remaining in a gas after it passes through the desiccant at the equilibrium velocity.[2] The drying efficiencies of several solid desiccants are compared in Table III. Barium oxide and magnesium perchlorate are the most efficient desiccants of those compared, whereas copper sulfate and granular calcium chloride are the least efficient. Recently, an extensive investigation by Trusell and Diehl evaluated the efficiencies of 21 desiccants in drying a stream of nitrogen.[3] Their results, which are listed in Table IV, show that the most efficient desiccant is anhydrous magnesium perchlorate.

The capacity of a desiccant is the amount of water it is able to remove per unit of the desiccant's dry weight. Often, a drying

Table III. Comparative efficiencies of various solid desiccants used in drying air.[a]

Desiccant	Granular form	Residual water[b] (mg/liter)
BaO	—	0.00065
$Mg(ClO_4)_2$	—	0.002
CaO	—	0.003
$CaSO_4$	Anhydrous	0.005
Al_2O_3	—	0.005
KOH	Sticks	0.014
Silica gel	—	0.030
$Mg(ClO_4)_2 \cdot 3H_2O$	—	0.031
$CaCl_2$	Dehydrated	0.36
NaOH	Sticks	0.80
$Ba(ClO_4)_2$	—	0.82
$ZnCl_2$	Sticks	0.98
$CaCl_2$	Technical anhydrous	1.25
$CaCl_2$	Granular	1.5
$CuSO_4$	Anhydrous	2.8

[a]Data taken from Reference 2.

[b]After drying to equilibrium.

Table IV. Comparative efficiencies and capacities of various solid desiccants in drying a stream of nitrogen.[a]

Desiccant	Initial composition	Regeneration requirements		Average efficiency[b] (mg/liter)	Relative capacity[c] (liters)
		Drying time (hr)	Temperature (°C)		
Anhydrous magnesium perchlorate[d]	$Mg(ClO_4)_2 \cdot 0.12H_2O$	48[e]	245[e]	0.0002	1168
Anhydrone[d,f]	$Mg(ClO_4)_2 \cdot 1.48H_2O$	—	240[g]	0.0015	1157
Barium oxide	96.2% BaO	—	1000[h]	0.0028	244
Activated alumina	Al_2O_3	6 to 8[i]	175, 400[i]	0.0029	263
Phosphorus pentoxide[j]	P_2O_5	—	—	0.0035	566
Molecular sieve 5A[f]	Calcium aluminum silicate	—	—	0.0039	215
Indicating anhydrous magnesium perchlorate[d]	88% $Mg(ClO_4)_2$ and 0.86% $KMnO_4$	48[e]	240[e,g]	0.0044	435
Anhydrous lithium perchlorate[j]	$LiClO_4$	12,[e] 12	70,[e] 110	0.013	267
Anhydrous calcium chloride[j]	$CaCl_2 \cdot 0.18H_2O$	16[e]	127[e]	0.067	33
Drierite[f]	$CaSO_4 \cdot 0.02H_2O$	1 to 2	200 to 225[k]	0.067	232
Silica gel	—	12	118 to 127[h]	0.070	317
Ascarite[f]	91.0% NaOH	—	—	0.093	44
Calcium chloride[j]	$CaCl_2 \cdot 0.28H_2O$	—	200[e]	0.099	57

Desiccant	Formula				
Anhydrous calcium chloride[j]	$CaCl_2$	16[e]	245[e]	0.137	31
Anhydrocel[f]	$CaSO_4 \cdot 0.21H_2O$	1 to 2	200 to 225[k]	0.207	683
Sodium hydroxide[j]	$NaOH \cdot 0.03H_2O$	—	—	0.513	178
Anhydrous barium perchlorate	$Ba(ClO_4)_2$	16	127	0.599	28
Calcium oxide	CaO	6	500, 900[g]	0.656	51
Magnesium oxide	MgO	6	800	0.753	22
Potassium hydroxide[j]	$KOH \cdot 0.52H_2O$	—	—	0.939	18.4
Mekohbite[f,j]	68.7% NaOH	—	—	1.378	68

[a] Nitrogen at an average flow rate of 225 ml/min was passed through a drying train consisting of three Swartz drying tubes (14 mm i.d. by 150 mm deep) maintained at 25°C. Except as noted in columns 3 and 4, the data in this table are taken from Reference 3.

[b] The average amount of water remaining in the nitrogen after it was dried to equilibrium.

[c] The average maximum volume of nitrogen dried at the specified efficiency for a given volume of desiccant.

[d] Hygroscopic.

[e] Dried in a vacuum.

[f] Trade name.

[g] Taken from Reference 4.

[h] Taken from Reference 5.

[i] Taken from Reference 6.

[j] Deliquescent.

[k] Taken from Reference 2.

13

agent is efficient but is unsuitable for drying large quantities of gas because of its limited capacity. Anhydrous calcium chloride is an example of such a desiccant. The capacity of a desiccant depends not only on the kind of material of which it is composed, but also on the size of the grains, the amount of surface area exposed to the gas, and the thickness through which the gas flows. Additional factors include the type of gas being dried as well as its velocity, temperature, pressure, and moisture content.[7] The capacities of several desiccants as a function of relative humidity are shown in Figure 2. The relative capacities of the most common drying agents can be determined from Table IV by comparing the volumes of gas each desiccant is able to dry. The materials with the highest capacities are anhydrous magnesium perchlorate, calcium sulfate, and phosphorus pentoxide.

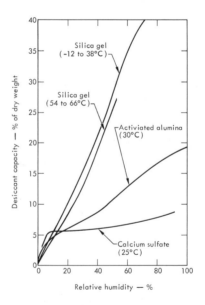

Figure 2. Desiccant capacity versus relative humidity for silica gel, activated alumina, and calcium sulfate (Drierite). The calcium-sulfate temperature is estimated. (Taken from Reference 5.)

One should not indiscriminately choose a desiccant simply because it has the proper efficiency and capacity. The geometry and size of the drying train must be considered to allow enough residence time to achieve equilibrium. In addition, many drying agents heat up violently when they are exposed to too much moisture over too short a time, and the pressure drop through the desiccant can be a problem at high flow rates. The most acceptable desiccants are anhydrous magnesium perchlorate, calcium sulfate, silica gel, and activated alumina. These are described below.

Anhydrous Magnesium Perchlorate

Anhydrous magnesium perchlorate (Anhydrone or Dehydrite) has the highest efficiency as well as the greatest capacity.[3] It is hygroscopic but not deliquescent, and it can absorb up to 35% of its own weight without evolving corrosive fumes as phosphorus pentoxide does. Since the monohydrate does not dissociate to liberate water until 134°C, it can be used to dry gases at high temperatures. Hydration continues until the hexahydrate, which has a theoretical capacity of 48.4%, is formed. Magnesium perchlorate is available in either the regular or the indicating form, the latter containing about 1% potassium permanganate.

The chief disadvantages of anhydrous magnesium perchlorate are its relatively high cost (roughly four times the cost of the other three desiccants, or about $8 a pound) and the difficulty of regenerating it. The temperature must be raised slowly while the perchlorate is dried in a vacuum in order to prevent the crystals from fusing. A final temperature of about 245° C is recommended to return the perchlorate to its anhydrous state.[3] A further disadvantage of this and other perchlorate desiccants is the tendency to form explosive compounds in the presence of organic materials, especially when they are heated.[6] Oil mists and other organic vapors must therefore be removed before such desiccants are used.

Calcium Sulfate

Calcium sulfate (Drierite or Anhydrocel) has an average efficiency of about 0.1 mg/liter and a capacity of 7 to 14% at 25°C. It is stable, inert, and not deliquescent, even at peak capacity. It is easily regenerated (1 to 2 hr at 200°C), and it operates at an almost constant efficiency over a wide range of temperatures. However, continued regeneration is difficult because the constant formation and destruction of the hemihydrate breaks down the grains. Calcium sulfate is available in sizes from 4 to 20 mesh and in either the regular or the indicating form.

Silica Gel

Silica gel has a moderately high efficiency and capacity because of its large number of capillary pores, which occupy about 50% of the gel's specific volume.[1] The capacity of the gel varies from batch to batch because of differences in the size and shape of the pores. The gel maintains its efficiency until it has absorbed 20% of its weight, and it can be regenerated indefinitely at 120°C. At this relatively low regeneration temperature, however, the gel cannot be used for high-temperature drying. If it is regenerated above 260°C, it loses some of its capacity. Silica gel is available in sizes from 2 to 300 mesh. The addition of cobalt chloride to the surface of the gel provides an indicating ability.

Activated Alumina

Activated alumina has a higher efficiency than silica gel but offers less capacity (12–14%), especially at high humidities. It can be regenerated between 180 and 400°C without losing much of its capacity. It is available in sizes from 14 mesh to 1 inch and in either the regular or the indicating form.

Liquid Desiccants

If solid desiccants are not practical, then liquid desiccants can be used. Liquid desiccants have a much higher capacity than their solid counterparts (see Figure 3), and they can be continuously

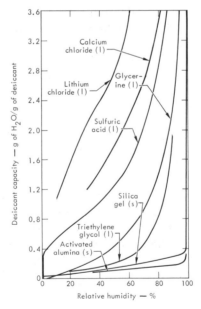

Figure 3. Desiccant capacity versus relative humidity for two solid desiccants and five liquid desiccants. (Taken from Reference 5.)

regenerated via spraying, pumping, or recirculating. On the other hand, their efficiencies are normally very low unless the anhydrous forms are used, and they usually cannot produce relative humidities below about 20%.[5] Some of the more common liquid desiccants are described in Table V. Note that although the strong acids and bases achieve the best efficiencies, they also emit corrosive vapors.

Cooling

Cooling is the most efficient laboratory method of removing water from a stream of gas. The gas is directed through a vessel in a low-temperature bath, and the excess water condenses on the cold walls of the vessel. As an example, a bath of dry ice and acetone at $-70°$ C removes all but about 0.01 mg/liter of water in

Table V.   Comparative properties of eight liquid desiccants.[a]

Desiccant	Relative humidity achieved at 21°C (%)	Solution concentration (%)	Operating temperature range (°C)	Remarks
Calcium chloride	20 to 25	40 to 50	32 to 49	None
Diethylene glycol	5 to 10	70 to 95	16 to 43	Can be regenerated with heating to 150°C
Glycerol	30 to 40[b]	70 to 80	21 to 38	Oxidizes and decomposes at high temperatures; can be regenerated with vacuum evaporation
Lithium chloride	10 to 20	30 to 45	21 to 38	None
Phosphoric acid	5 to 20	80 to 95	16 to 38	Corrosive; fumes carried over during the drying process; does not fume during regeneration
Sodium and potassium hydroxides	10 to 20	Saturated	29 to 49	Corrosive; frequently used to remove CO_2 and water simultaneously
Sulfuric acid	5 to 20	60 to 70	21 to 49	Corrosive; most efficient liquid desiccant
Triethylene glycol	5 to 10	70 to 95	16 to 43	None

[a]Data taken from Reference 1.

[b]5% with anhydrous diethylene glycol.

air at equilibrium. A liquid-nitrogen bath at $-194°$ C removes all but about 1 x 10^{-23} mg/liter of water in air at equilibrium. This is about 19 orders of magnitude more efficient than anhydrous magnesium perchlorate, the best solid desiccant.

REMOVAL OF PARTICULATES

There are a number of in-line filters that remove micron-sized particles. One example is a sintered-bronze mesh 1 inch in diameter and 2.5 inches long that can filter out 2-μ particles at a flow rate of 1 ft³/min and an operating pressure of 110 psi.[8] Filters made of metal fibers (pore size = 5 to 750μ),[9] sintered stainless steel (pore size = 2 to 150μ),[10] and foamed metals (pore size = 5μ to 0.1 in.)[11] are available. Porous Teflon and Kel-F filters that can remove particles as small as 2 μ are also available.[12]

If removal down to certain precise particle sizes is required, membrane filters are often useful. These are available in sizes from 13 to 293 mm with pore sizes from 75 Å (7.5 mμ) to 8 μ.[13-15] These filters are constructed from a wide selection of microporous materials (*e.g.*, regenerated cellulose, polyvinyl chloride, glass fibers, and polypropylene) whose capacities are accurately known.[13] The flow rate per unit of filter area at a given temperature is a function of the pore size and the upstream pressure. The relationship between pressure, pore size, and flow rate for a typical membrane filter is shown in Figure 4.

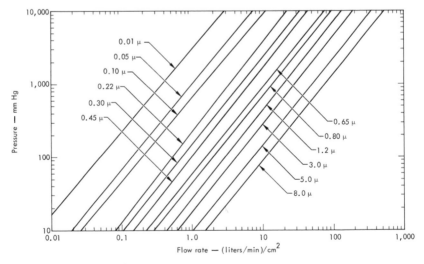

Figure 4. Pressure versus flow rate for 12 mean pore sizes at 25°C. (Taken from Reference 15.)

REMOVAL OF ORGANIC VAPORS

Organic vapors such as unburned hydrocarbons are sometimes present in a compressor-generated gas even after it has been passed through an in-line filter. The concentrations of such organic vapors can be further reduced either by passing the gas through an activated-charcoal filter or by continuously burning the vapors in a combustion furnace.

Activated coconut charcoal has long been the most popular material for removing organic vapors. Instead of water vapor being adsorbed on the filter, the organic vapors tend to displace any water that may be present. Coconut charcoal has internal submicroscopic capillaries that are just slightly larger than the molecules they trap. A filter containing fine grains of coconut charcoal uniformly dispersed throughout a web matrix is also available.[16] Not all organic vapors are completely adsorbed by charcoal filters, even when large filter areas and low flow rates are used. For example, such low molecular weight compounds as acetylene, ethane, ethylene, methane, hydrogen, carbon monoxide, and carbon dioxide have almost no affinity for activated charcoal.[17]

As for the second method of removing organic vapors, Kusnetz *et al.* recommend passing the gas through a 2-inch-diameter Mullite tube that is filled with copper shavings and surrounded by a combustion furnace maintained at $1250°$ F.[18] The exiting gas is cooled to $800°$ F by a finned brass tube and a water-cooled condenser. To remove the combustion products, the gas is bubbled through a sulfuric acid–dichromate solution and passed through filters of Ascarite, activated charcoal, and glass wool, in that order.

REMOVAL OF MISCELLANEOUS CONTAMINANTS

A host of in-line filters are available for treating compressed gases in the laboratory. These filters can remove both water and oil mists as well as particles as small as 1μ. Drain plugs are provided for periodically removing the collected liquid, and the filters themselves can be exchanged when they become clogged or excessively loaded. Automatic drain traps are also available.[19] Most compressed-gas filters operate via a two-stage separation that involves centrifugal or inertial separation followed by diffusion through a filter [20-22] or a special absorption material.[23]

Compressed gases may also contain acid gases, carbon monoxide, and carbon dioxide. The acid gases are those that produce hydrogen ions either by direct dissociation or by hydrolysis and include hydrogen cyanide, hydrogen chloride, and sulfur dioxide.

Both acid gases and carbon dioxide can be filtered out by soda lime, a mixture of calcium and sodium hydroxides. Soda lime with various moisture contents is available in sizes from 4 to 14 mesh, in either the regular or the indicating form, and can absorb up to 25% of its weight of carbon dioxide. The rate at which acid gases are absorbed by soda lime depends on the condition of the lime. As the lime becomes spent, a thin film of calcium carbonate covers the surface of the soda lime particles and cannot be removed by regeneration.

Both carbon dioxide and water vapor can be absorbed by Ascarite, which consists of sodium hydroxide in a woven asbestos matrix. Ascarite is available in sizes from 8 to 30 mesh.

Carbon monoxide is relatively unaffected by its passage through soda lime, activated carbon, or the previously described desiccants, so special provisions for its removal must be made. Hopcalite, usually a mixture of copper and manganese oxides, has traditionally been the most practical agent for removing carbon monoxide. It operates as a catalytic oxidizing agent, converting the carbon monoxide to carbon dioxide which can ultimately be absorbed by Ascarite or soda lime. The main requirement for using Hopcalite is that it be kept scrupulously dry, for it loses its catalytic ability in the presence of water. Other carbon monoxide filters are also available commercially.[23]

For the removal of specific substances, the appropriate sorbents are listed in Reference 24.

Chapter 3

Flow-Rate and
Volume Measurements

Flow-rate and volume measurements play an important role in the production of both static and dynamic gas mixtures. The accuracy with which gases are mixed is often directly dependent on the accuracy of the flow-rate and volume measurements. Hence, in order to minimize errors in gas-measuring systems, one must thoroughly understand the methods and characteristics of flow-rate and volume measurements.

This chapter deals with flow rates between a fraction of a milliliter per minute and several cubic feet per minute and does not cover the higher flow rates (100 ft³/min or more) that are often encountered in industrial ventilation systems. Primary, intermediate, and secondary laboratory standards are discussed, and a complete spectrum of devices for measuring flow rates and volumes in the laboratory is evaluated.

PRIMARY STANDARDS

Spirometers

Spirometers or bell-type provers are the most accurate standards for flow-rate and volume measurements. They come in a variety of sizes. Nine liters and 2, 5, 10, and 20 ft³ are a few of the available volumes.[25, 26] A representative spirometer is shown in Figure 5.

21

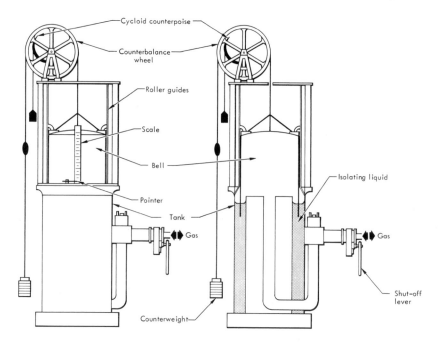

Figure 5. Orthographic and cross-sectional views of a 5-ft³ spirometer.

The spirometer functions as follows. When a gas enters the inlet, the moveable bell of precisely known dimensions rises. The bell is supported by a chain, balanced by a counterweight, and separated from the stationary tank by a liquid interface, often a light oil. A volume scale, fixed to the side of the bell, and a pointer, attached to the stationary tank, indicate the total volume entering the tank over a given time interval. A pressure differential of 2 inches H_2O is usually all that is required to raise or lower the bell. The downward pressure exerted by the bell, regardless of the depth it is submerged in the liquid, is kept essentially constant by a cycloid counterpoise that automatically compensates for buoyancy changes exerted by the liquid media.[27] Thus, the bell requires the same pressure to raise or lower it over its entire working range. The temperatures of the liquid and the ambient air as well as differences in the working pressure are measured with the attached thermometers and oil manometer.

Most spirometers are individually calibrated against "cubic-foot" bottles° at the factory,[28] but they can be rechecked if minor inaccuracies are suspected. Before a spirometer is checked, it

°A cubic-foot bottle is a vessel that is certified by the U.S. Bureau of Standards to have a volume of exactly 1 ft³.

must be properly aligned, the liquid level must be correct, all leaks must be eliminated, and the difference between the temperature of the isolating liquid and the temperature of the ambient air must not be more than 0.5° F.[29]

The first step in calibrating a spirometer is to see if the bell drifts when all valves are open. If it does, the counterweight should be adjusted accordingly. In models that do not have a cycloid counterpoise, the bell should drift toward the geometric center of the raised bell from both the fully raised and the fully lowered positions.[30] The spirometer can now be checked by means of a cubic-foot bottle or, more conveniently, by means of a "strapping" procedure that consists of measuring the bell's dimensions with a steel tape and calculating the volume.[29]

Figure 6 gives an illustration of the strapping technique. The bell is shown both in the fully raised or zero scale position (Figure 6A) and the empty or 100 scale position (Figure 6B). Volume measurements at both bell positions are made at the same pressure differential between the inside and outside of the bell. The gas volume, v_G, displaced when the bell is moved from the raised to the empty position is equal to the volume of the bell interior,

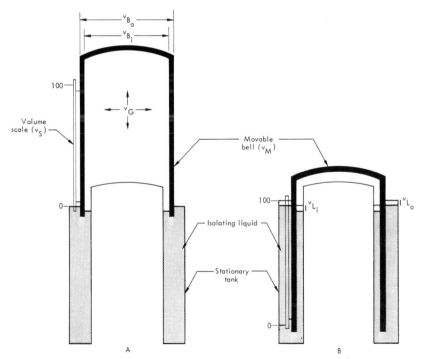

Figure 6. Simplified cross-section of a spirometer with the bell fully raised (A) and fully lowered (B).

v_{B_i}, between the reference marks plus the liquid volume, v_{L_i}, which is caused by bell displacement. The interior bell volume, v_{B_i}, is in turn equal to the exterior bell volume, v_{B_o}, minus the volume of the metal bell, v_M. The volume of the metal bell plus the scale volume, v_S, is equal to the liquid which rises inside, v_{L_i}, and outside, v_{L_o}, the bell. These relationships can be also shown as:[29]

$$v_G = v_{B_i} + v_{L_i}, \tag{25}$$

$$v_{B_i} = v_{B_o} - v_M, \tag{26}$$

and

$$v_M + v_S = v_{L_o} + v_{L_i}. \tag{27}$$

By combining Equations 25, 26, and 27 and solving for v_G, we obtain

$$v_G = v_{B_o} + v_S - v_{L_o}. \tag{28}$$

EXAMPLE 1. By means of the strapping technique, calculate the percentage of error in the volume scale on a five-cubic-foot spirometer.[29]

Measurements

Outside diameter of the bell	66.047 in.
Length of the volume scale	25.031 in.
Width of the volume scale	1.125 in.
Thickness of the volume scale	0.117 in.
Thickness of the measuring tape	0.006 in.
Distance between the outer surface of the bell and the inner surface of the stationary tank	1.942 in.
Rise in the level of the isolating liquid for full travel of the bell	0.345 in.

Calculations

Corrected outside diameter of the bell, 66.047 in. − (3.14 × 0.006 in.)	66.028 in.
Actual outside diameter of the bell, $\dfrac{66.028 \text{ in.}}{3.1416}$	21.017 in.

Volume of the bell as calculated from
the actual outside diameter,

$$\frac{3.1416 \times \left(\frac{21.017\ in.}{2}\right)^2 \times 25.031\ in.}{1728\ in.^3/ft^3} \qquad 5.0254\ ft^3$$

Volume of the volume scale,

$$\frac{25.031\ in. \times 1.125\ in. \times 0.117\ in.}{1728\ in.^3/ft^3} \qquad 0.0019\ ft^3$$

Diameter of the stationary tank at the level of the liquid,

$$21.017\ in. + (2 \times 1.942\ in.) \qquad 24.901\ in.$$

Difference in the apparent volume of the liquid,

$$\frac{3.1416 \times \left[\left(\frac{24.901\ in.}{2}\right)^2 - \left(\frac{21.017\ in.}{2}\right)^2\right] \times 0.345\ in.}{1728\ in.^3/ft^3}$$

$$0.0280\ ft^3$$

Volume of the displaced gas,

$$5.0254\ ft^3 + 0.0019\ ft^3 - 0.0280\ ft^3 \qquad 4.9993\ ft^3$$

Volume scale too short by

$$\frac{5.0000\ ft^3 - 4.9993\ ft^3}{5.0000\ ft^3} \times 100 \qquad 0.014\%$$

The strapping method is often as good as a cubic-foot bottle,
and it routinely yields accuracies of ±0.2% when it is performed
by an experienced person.

Pitot Tubes

The primary standard for measuring gas velocities is the Pitot
tube. This device is particularly useful for measuring high flows in
large ducts and is primarily used in ventilation work, but it does
have some laboratory applications. Pitot tubes are extensively described in the literature;[31,32] thus the following section presents
only the most basic concepts.

Basically, a Pitot tube is a pressure-sensing instrument. The
standard Pitot tube adopted by the American Conference of Governmental Industrial Hygienists is shown in Figure 7. It consists
of two concentric tubes—an inner one that senses the impact

pressure of a flowing gas and an outer one that senses the static pressure. In order for a Pitot tube to function properly, the orifice in the upstream end of the tube must face the flow squarely. The impact and static pressures can be measured with an upright U-tube, an inclined manometer, or some other suitable pressure-measuring device, depending on the magnitude of the pressure and velocity. When a U-tube is employed, acceptable accuracies can be achieved only at velocities above 2500 ft/min. On the other hand, a carefully made and accurately leveled inclined manometer can retain its accuracy at velocities as low as 600 ft/min.[32,33] Some typical velocity pressures and velocities are 0.062 in. H_2O at 100 ft/min, 0.14 in. at 1500 ft/min, 0.25 in. at 2000 ft/min, and 0.56 in. at 3000 ft/min.[30]

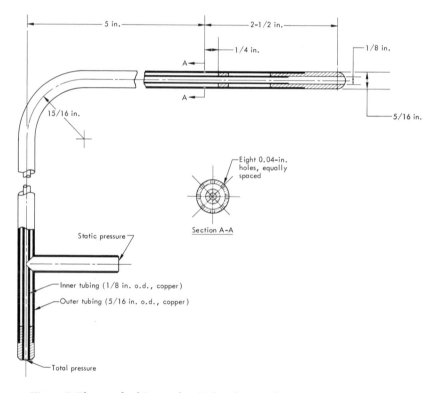

Figure 7. The standard Pitot tube. (Taken from Reference 30.)

Since Pitot tubes contain no moving parts, they can be used in almost any position or location. If they are made of stainless steel, they can be used at high temperatures and pressures and even in corrosive atmospheres. Gases that contain particles, aerosols, or fumes must be avoided because such contaminants may foul the small, carefully machined orifices.

The amount of air flowing through a duct can be calculated from the basic equation

$$Q = A\bar{u} \,, \tag{29}$$

where Q is the flow rate of the gas (in cubic feet per minute), A is the cross-sectional area of the duct (in square feet), and $\bar{u}$ is the average linear velocity of the gas (in feet per minute). When a Pitot tube is used, $\bar{u}$ is determined by

$$\bar{u} = \left(\frac{2p}{\rho}\right)^{\frac{1}{2}} \,, \tag{30}$$

where p is the difference between the impact and static pressures and ρ is the density of the gas.

Since the velocity of a gas in a given duct varies across any given cross section because of frictional losses and the shape of the duct, many measurements must be made to determine the most accurate average velocity.[32] However, one can closely approximate the average velocity by assuming that it is roughly 90% of the velocity in the center of the duct. Equation 29 then becomes

$$Q = 0.9 \, A\left(\frac{2p}{\rho}\right)^{\frac{1}{2}} \,. \tag{31}$$

If greater accuracy is desired, the traversing technique described in Reference 32 can be used.

Frictionless Pistons

Although spirometers and wet test meters* are useful standards, their accuracy diminishes at flow rates of 1 liter/min or less. To fill this gap, soap-bubble meters[34] and mercury-sealed pistons[35] have been devised. These instruments measure flow rates of 1 to 1000 ml/min with reasonable accuracy and are used to check the accuracy of secondary standards, particularly rotameters, critical orifices, and porous plugs.

Two kinds of soap-bubble meters are shown in Figure 8. Gas from the instrument being calibrated enters the inlet and travels up the buret, whose capacity of 10, 50, 100, or 250 ml depends on the needed range. Soap bubbles are introduced by squeezing the

*Wet test meters are described under "Intermediate Standards."

rubber bulb and raising the soap solution above the inlet. The gas rises through the solution, forming bubbles, and the progress of the bubbles between selected volume markings is timed with a stop watch. As the bubbles rise, they act essentially as frictionless pistons, for a pressure of 0.02 in. H_2O is all that is required to raise the bubbles at a uniform rate.[36]

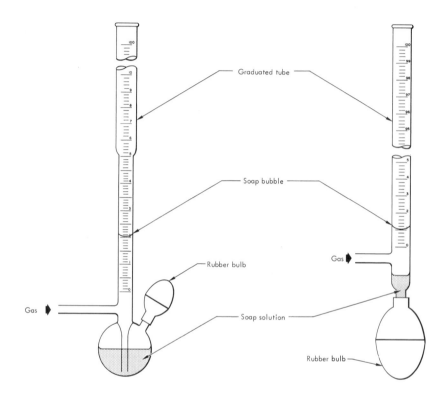

Figure 8. Two kinds of soap-bubble meters for measuring low gas flows.

Under average laboratory conditions, soap-bubble meters are usually accurate to within 1%. However, with carefully controlled conditions and for relatively nonreactive and insoluble gases, accuracies of ±0.25% have been reported.[37] The accuracy of soap-bubble meters can be improved slightly[38] by adding photoelectric devices[39,40] or electrical contacts[41] that actuate relays and timers. As the flow rate approaches 1 or 2 ml/min, the accuracy declines because of gas permeation through the soap film. For example, Czubryt and Gesser report errors of 3 and 7% respectively for carbon dioxide and argon flowing at 1.6 and 1.2 ml/min.[42]

If a soap-bubble meter is undesirable, then a precisely measured and calibrated electronically actuated piston may be used.[43] Noble reports that such a device has an accuracy of ±0.03% at flow rates between 1 and 100 ml/min.[38]

A commercially available instrument for calibrating low-flow meters is the mercury-sealed piston shown in Figure 9. The gas enters the precision-bore glass cylinder and displaces the polyvinyl chloride piston, which is made gas-tight by the mercury O-ring. This instrument is virtually frictionless, but the weight of the piston must be compensated for in order to achieve the best accuracy. The capacity of this instrument ranges from 1 to 24,000 ml/min, and its accuracy is ±0.2% for timing intervals of 30 seconds or more.[35]

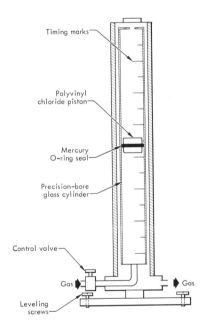

Figure 9. Mercury-sealed piston for measuring low gas flows.

Aspirator Bottles

Flow rates of 10 to 500 ml/min can often be measured with an aspirator bottle like that shown in Figure 10. Gas from the secondary standard being calibrated flows into the aspirator bottle, which is filled with water. The water is then displaced into the graduated cylinder. The time required to displace a set volume of water gives the flow rate. The flow rate should be corrected either to standard conditions or to the temperature and pressure noted on the data sheet. Aspirator bottles do not have as wide an appeal as soap-bubble meters because they demonstrate less accuracy (± 1 or 2%), convenience, and range.

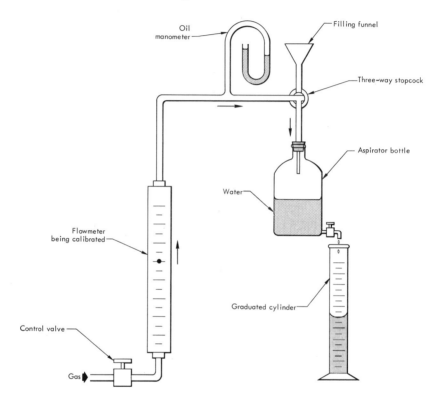

Figure 10. Aspirator bottle for measuring low gas flows.

INTERMEDIATE STANDARDS

Reasonable accuracy in volume or flow measurements does not necessarily require the use of primary standards, for there are several intermediate standards that are almost as effective. Although the internal volumes of intermediate standards cannot always be obtained by dimensional measurements (hence the intermediate rating), such standards still exhibit accuracies of $\pm 1\%$ or better and can therefore be used with confidence. Intermediate standards include the wet test meter and the dry gas meter.

Wet Test Meters

A wet test meter is shown in Figure 11. It consists of a container which houses a revolving drum that is about two-thirds submerged in water. The drum is divided into four sections, each of which has an inlet and an outlet. When a gas enters the meter, it exerts a buoyant force that turns the drum clockwise. As one quadrant becomes full, a new quadrant rotates into the filling position and the full one begins expelling gas through its outlet. The drum rotates smoothly if the gas is fed to the meter at a steady rate. The total volume for a given time interval is recorded by the decade dials provided. Attached to the meter are a water manometer for measuring the internal and external pressure differential and a thermometer for measuring the temperature of the incoming gas. The filling funnel and the drain and fill cocks are used to keep the water level at the calibration point.

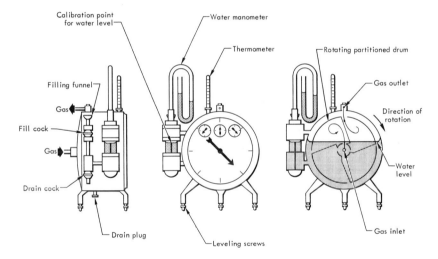

Figure 11. Side, front, and cross-sectional views of a wet test meter.

The minimum and maximum flow rates of wet test meters are usually 1 and 80 liters/min respectively. Lower flow rates generally result in unacceptable friction losses, and higher flow rates cause excessive pressure differentials. Wet test meters are mostly used to calibrate secondary standards, but they can also be used to meter gases directly.[44]

Before a wet test meter can be checked for accuracy, it must be leveled and filled with water to the calibration point. Then the gas should be run through the meter for several hours in order to saturate the water and allow the meter to equilibrate.[30] The meter can then be checked against a 0.1-ft³ bottle[45,46] or against a spirometer as shown in Figure 12. Table VI gives a sample data sheet using a spirometer as a primary standard. The starting volume, the atmospheric pressure, the temperature of the gas, and the pressure inside the wet test meter are all recorded. Enough gas is withdrawn to significantly displace the bell in the spirometer and to make the drum in the wet test meter revolve three times. During the calibration period any pressure differentials revealed by the water manometers are recorded.

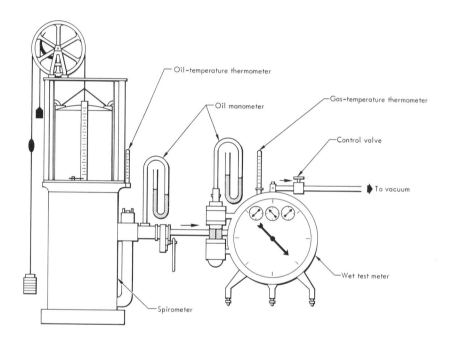

Figure 12. Setup for calibrating a wet test meter against a spirometer.

Each calibration point is repeated three or more times at various flow rates so that a curve relating flow rate to error can be drawn. The volume measurements are corrected to standard conditions, but water-vapor effects are usually ignored.[30] Wet test meters should check out to within 0.5% of the values indicated by the volume dials and new instruments are often within 0.25%.[47]

Table VI. Sample data sheet for the calibration of a wet test meter with air.[a]

	Trial No.			
	1	2	3	4
Spirometer data[b]				
Initial reading, A_s (ft^3)	2.000	2.500	2.000	2.100
Final reading, B_s (ft^3)	2.692	3.262	2.746	2.828
Volume, C_s (liters)[c]	19.61	21.58	20.64	23.45
Manometer reading, D_s (in. H_2O)	0.015	0.025	0.040	0.045
Corrected volume, E_s (liters)[d]	20.07	22.09	21.13	24.00
Duration of run, F_s (min)	18.65	10.50	5.630	3.000
Flow rate, G_s (liters/min)[e]	1.076	2.104	3.753	8.000
Wet-test-meter data[f]				
Initial reading, A_w (ft^3)	2.500	3.000	2.000	2.500
Final reading, B_w (ft^3)	3.195	3.763	2.728	3.327
Apparent volume, C_w (liters)[c]	19.68	21.60	20.62	23.42
Manometer reading, D_w (in. H_2O)	0.2	0.5	1.2	2.3
Corrected apparent volume, E_w (liters)[d]	20.14	22.08	21.05	23.84
Duration of run, F_w (min)	18.65	10.50	5.630	3.000
Apparent flow rate, G_w liters/min)[e]	1.080	2.103	3.739	7.947
Error, H_w (%)[g]	-0.37	0.05	0.37	0.75

[a]Room temperature = 23°C, atmospheric pressure = 745 mm Hg. Standard conditions = 22°C and 760 mm Hg.

[b]Temperature of the spirometer liquid = 23°C.

[c]$C_{s,w} = (B_{s,w} - A_{s,w}) \times 28.32$ liters/ft^3.

[d]$E_{s,w} = \dfrac{296°K \times 760 \text{ mm Hg}}{295°K \times \{745 \text{ mm Hg} + [(1.87 \text{ mm Hg/in. } H_2O) \times D_{s,w}]\}}$.

[e]$G_{s,w} = E_{s,w}/F_{s,w}$.

[f]Temperature of the gas (air) = 23°C.

[g]$H_w = [(G_s - G_w)/G_s] \times 100$.

Dry Gas Meters

The dry gas meter is a common industrial device that can easily be adapted to the laboratory. Such meters can measure flow rates of 5 to 5000 liters/min at pressures of up to 250 lb/in.² with an accuracy of a few per cent.[28,48]

Figure 13 shows a cross section of a dry gas meter. The meter consists of a sealed outer case, two sliding valves, two bellows, several volume dials, and a linkage system. In Figure 13A, the gas enters the meter and passes the left-hand sliding valve, filling the left-hand bellows and forcing gas out of the chamber on the left. When this bellows is fully extended, the sliding valves shift and direct the incoming gas to the right-hand bellows. This forces the gas from the right-hand chamber as shown in Figure 13B. When both bellows are fully extended, the sliding valves again shift and the bellows empty separately as shown in Figures 13C and 13D. This cycle of alternately filling and emptying the bellows is linked to the volume dials, which register the corresponding volume changes.

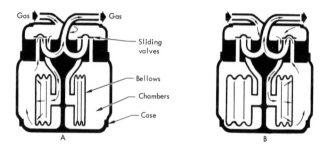

Figure 13. Idealized cross section of a dry gas meter. The operation of this instrument is described in the text.

Dry gas meters can be calibrated in the same way as wet test meters but their usual accuracies are about ±1%. If the recorded flow rate differs from the actual flow rate by more than 2%, it can be made to correspond more closely by means of the tangential adjusting weights which influence the motion of the linkage to the volume dials.

SECONDARY STANDARDS

Most flow-measurement devices used in the laboratory are classified as secondary standards. That is, they have been compared against a primary standard at known conditions of gas type, pressure, and temperature and have a calibration curve relating meter reading to actual flow rate.

Secondary standards, usually not as accurate as their primary counterparts, are nevertheless useful because of their convenient size, weight, cost, and general availability. These standards include volumetric flowmeters, such as rotameters, orifice meters, critical orifices, and porous plugs, and air-velocity meters, which include heated wires and thermocouples as well as electromechanical systems such as drag-body flowmeters.

Volumetric Flowmeters

The most 'popular devices for measuring flow rates are the volumetric flowmeters. Well over 100 types are commercially available, and these have been summarized in several buyer's guides.[49,50] These flowmeters are available in a wide variety of flow rates and temperature and pressure ranges, and periodic tabulations of their specifications have been published.[51,62]

Rotameters

The most widely used laboratory method for measuring gas or liquid flow rates is the rotameter or variable-area flowmeter. It is usually a round glass tube of increasing diameter which houses one or more floats which are free to move vertically up and down the tube axis. On the sides are permanently engraved reference marks which may be either linearly or exponentially inscribed on the tube. Figure 14 gives an example. As the gas flows up the tube, the float is displaced and continues to move upward until equilibrium is reached. This occurs when the downward force of the float just equals the buoyant force of the moving gas stream. Any change in the flow rate will cause the float to occupy a proportionally different position.

The flow-rate range of a full set of rotameters is enormous and spans from 1 ml/min to over 300 ft³/min with reasonable accuracy. The range of each individual rotameter, however, is considerably less and is usually about one-and-a-half to two orders of magnitude. The range can be extended by using multiple floats, and many commercial types are equipped with dual floats of glass and stainless steel.

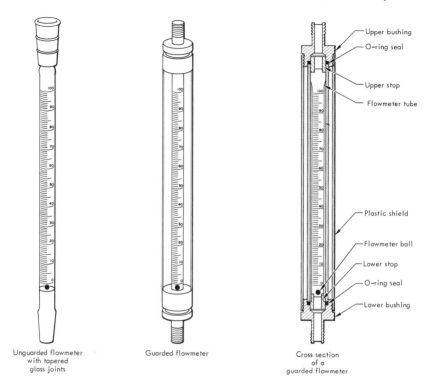

Unguarded flowmeter
with tapered
glass joints

Guarded flowmeter

Cross section
of a
guarded flowmeter

Figure 14. Two kinds of rotameters.

Float design will vary depending on the manufacturer and the flow rate desired. Most lower range rotameters will use spherical floats, but a wide variety of configurations exist, especially at higher flow rates. Figure 15 shows several types of floats currently in use. No matter which type is used, the rotameter reading is conventionally taken at the widest point of the float.[53] For example, spherical types are usually read at the center and not at the top or bottom of the float.

Some commercial flowmeters have not only a dual range but also the capacity to measure the total volume through a system over a given time interval. A volume counter is linked to a turbine wheel whose spin is proportional to the amount of gas turning it. This works well when the flow-rate changes are gradual, but significant errors arise when sharp pulses and fast flow-rate changes are encountered.

Most rotameters are calibrated at room temperature and pressure, but they may be corrected to the experimental conditions by

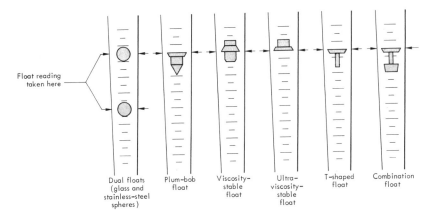

, **Figure 15.** Six kinds of rotameter floats. Readings are conventionally taken at the widest point of the float.

using the appropriate equations. Pressures of 0.5–5 atm and temperatures from 0–150° C are not unreasonable conditions of use.

Rotameters are available with a wide variety of inlet and outlet connections. Hose barbs, pipe thread, and ball and tapered glass joints are commercially supplied. Many times it is best to purchase enclosed flowmeters either in single units in plastic tubes (as shown in Figure 14) or in multiple units in a protective case to minimize the possibility of breakage. These jacketed flowmeters can be connected in series or parallel[54] to extend the desired range. This is shown in Figure 16.

The flow rate of a gas through a rotameter is seldom calculated from tube diameters and float dimensions, although the development and use of such equations are adequately covered in the literature.[55-60] Instead, curves relating meter reading to flow rate are derived from a calibration against one of the primary or intermediate standards discussed, usually a bubble meter, spirometer, or wet test meter. Although the manufacturer generally provides reasonably accurate calibration curves, rotameters should be recalibrated at the experimental conditions of interest with the primary standard on either the inlet or the outlet and open to the atmosphere as shown in Figure 17. In this manner the flow condition at a known temperature, T_1, and pressure P_1, are known and the actual conditions (P_2 and T_2) need not be known. Once this basic information is available, correction factors for changes in pressure, temperature, and test gas can be more realistically applied.

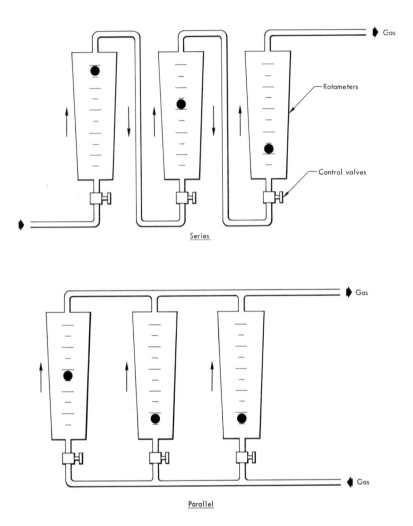

Figure 16. Rotameters arranged in series and in parallel.

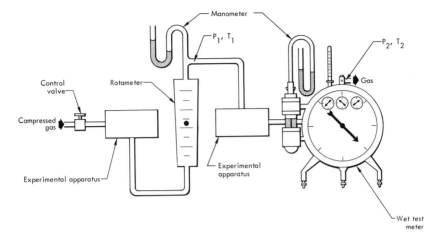

Figure 17. Setup for calibrating a rotameter against a wet test meter.

Corrections for variations of pressure and temperature which differ from the initial rotameter calibration for a tube of linear range (usually specified at 760 mm Hg and 21°C) is given by

$$Q_{T_2 P_2} = Q_{T_1 P_1} \left(\frac{P_2 T_1}{P_1 T_2} \right)^{\frac{1}{2}}, \qquad (32)$$

where

$Q_{T_2 P_2}$ = gas flow rate at the experimental temperature and pressure,

$Q_{T_1 P_1}$ = gas flow rate at the calibration temperature and pressure,

T_2, P_2 = experimental temperature and pressure, and

T_1, P_1 = calibration temperature and pressure.

EXAMPLE 2. A rotameter calibrated at 760 mm Hg and 21°C is to be used at 2.00 atm and 50°C. What flow rate must be read from the calibration curve to achieve 800 ml/min at the new temperature and pressure condition?

$$Q_{T_1 P_1} = (800 \text{ ml/min}) \left[\frac{(2 \text{ atm})(294°K)}{(1 \text{ atm})(323°K)} \right]^{-\frac{1}{2}} = 593 \text{ ml/min.}$$

Often it is desirable to use a flowmeter for gases other than the one for which it has been calibrated. If the experimental gas densities are known (some are tabulated in Appendix E), then

$$Q_2 = Q_1 \left(\frac{\rho_1}{\rho_2}\right)^{\frac{1}{2}} , \tag{33}$$

where

Q_2 =   flow rate of the test gas,

Q_1 =   flow rate of the calibrated gas,

ρ_1 =   experimental density of the calibrated gas, and

ρ_2 =   experimental density of the test gas.

EXAMPLE 3. A rotameter reads 6.10 when 1.00 ft³/min of air flows. What is the flow rate in liters per minute of nitrous oxide (N_2O) at the same conditions and float reading? The experimental densities at 760 mm Hg and 0°C for air and nitrous oxide (from Appendix E) are respectively 1.2929 and 1.978 g/liter.

$$Q_{N_2O} = 1.00 \text{ ft}^3/\text{min} \times 28.3 \text{ liters}/\text{ft}^3$$

$$\times \left(\frac{1.2929 \text{ g/liter}}{1.978 \text{ g/liter}}\right)^{\frac{1}{2}} = 22.9 \text{ liters}/\text{min}.$$

EXAMPLE 4. The following calibration data have been determined for air at 740 mm Hg and 23°C:

Reading	Flow rate (liters/ min)	Reading	Flow rate (liters/ min)
1.25	0.50	4.00	3.00
2.00	1.00	4.55	3.50
2.45	1.50	4.90	4.00
2.90	2.00	5.50	4.50
3.55	2.50	6.00	5.00

Calculate and plot the data obtained when the rotameter is used for air and xenon at 560 mm Hg and 100°C and for xenon at 740 mm Hg and 23°C.

For air and xenon at 560 mm Hg and 100°C,

$$Q_{560 \text{ mm}, 100°C} = \left(Q_{740 \text{ mm}, 23°C}\right)$$

$$\left(\frac{560 \text{ mm} \times 296°K}{740 \text{ mm} \times 373°K}\right)^{\frac{1}{2}} = Q_{740 \text{ mm}, 23°C} \times 0.775.$$

For xenon at 740 mm Hg and 23°C,

$$Q_{Xe} = Q_{air} \times \left(\frac{1.2929 \text{ g/liter}}{5.897 \text{ g/liter}}\right)^{\frac{1}{2}} = Q_{air} \times 0.468 .$$

A flow-rate table can be constructed (see Table VII), and the data are plotted in Figure 18.

Table VII. Solution to example 4.

Rotameter reading	Air flow rate (in liters/min) at:		Xenon flow rate (in liters/min) at:	
	23°C, 740 mm Hg	100°C 560 mm Hg	23°C, 740 mm Hg	100°C, 560 mm Hg
1.25	0.50	0.39	0.23	0.18
2.10	1.00	0.78	0.47	0.36
2.45	1.50	1.16	0.70	0.54
2.90	2.00	1.55	0.94	0.73
3.55	2.50	1.94	1.17	0.91
4.00	3.00	2.33	1.40	1.09
4.55	3.50	2.71	1.63	1.26
4.90	4.00	3.10	1.87	1.45
5.50	4.50	3.48	2.11	1.63
6.00	5.00	3.87	2.34	1.81

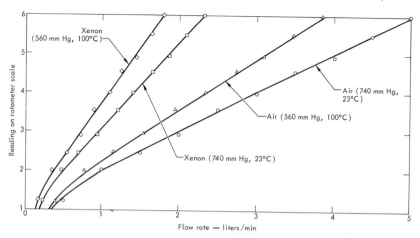

Figure 18. Solution to Example 4.

In some rotameters, the range of the tube is exponential rather than linear. Corrections for variation in pressure and temperature are then made somewhat differently, using the expression

$$Q_{T_2 P_2} = Q_{T_1 P_1} \left(\frac{P_2}{P_1}\right) \left(\frac{T_1}{T_2}\right)^{1.5} . \tag{34}$$

If another gas is to be used and no calibration is to be carried out, the relationship between the gas flow rates is

$$Q_1 = Q_2 \left(\frac{\eta_2}{\eta_1}\right), \tag{35}$$

where $\eta_{1,2}$ are the gas viscosities in centipoises at standard conditions.

Rotameters offer the simplest, most inexpensive method of measuring the great range of flows encountered in gas-mixing systems. Manufacturers of these devices generally supply typical calibration curves with their instruments which indicate that accuracies of ±5% should be routinely attained. However, if best results are desired, the rotameter should be recalibrated in the system and accuracies of ±1–2% of full scale can be routinely achieved. Calibration curves can be calculated for other gases at different temperatures and pressures with good results as long as one reliable curve is known and the gas densities or viscosities at the experimental conditions of interest are known.

Orifice Meters

One of the oldest devices of flow-rate measurement is the orifice meter. It has long been used to meter moving gas streams at flow rates from a maximum of 50 liters/min down to several milliliters per minute if special techniques are employed.

A typical orifice meter is shown in Figure 19. A restrictive orifice, usually a capillary, is placed in the moving gas stream. The pressure differential created by the movement of gas through the orifice is related almost directly to the flow rate over a specified pressure range. The pressure can be measured with any of the normal devices available, and U-tubes containing mercury, water, or light oil and inclined manometers are popular devices. The flow rate-pressure relationship is usually determined experimentally and the calibration displayed graphically as shown in Figure 19.

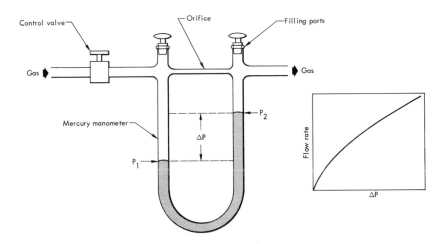

Figure 19. Sketch of a typical orifice meter and a calibration curve correlating the meter's readings with flow rate.

The flow rate can be calculated from Equation 36. According to Poiseuille's law, the flow of gas through a tube, neglecting kinetic effects at the entrance and exit of the capillary tube, is[61,62]

$$Q = \frac{(P_1 - P_2)\left(1 + \dfrac{P_1 - P_2}{2P_2}\right)}{r},$$

(36)

where

$$r = \frac{128 \times \eta L}{\pi d^4} , \tag{37}$$

Q   =   flow rate (cm³/sec),

P_1 =   upstream pressure (dyne/cm²),

P_2 =   downstream pressure (dyne/cm²),

r   =   capillary flow resistance (g/cm⁴-sec),

L   =   capillary length (cm),

d   =   internal capillary diameter (cm),

η =   viscosity of gas (poise or g/cm-sec), and

π =   3.1416.

The viscosities of several common gases are shown in Table VIII at the conditions normally encountered.

EXAMPLE 5. Calculate the flow rate in liters of nitric oxide per minute through a glass capillary tube. The upstream and down-stream pressures are 20 and 14.7 lb/in.² respectively. The capillary is 1 in. long and has a 0.1-mm inside diameter. The room temperature is 20°C.

$$r = \frac{128 \times (1.876 \times 10^{-4} \text{ g/cm-sec}) \times 1.0 \text{ in.} \times 2.54 \text{ cm/in.}}{3.14 \times (0.01 \text{cm})^4}$$

$$= 1.94 \times 10^6 \text{ g/cm}^4\text{-sec.}$$

If $P_1 - P_2 = (20.0 \text{ lb/in.}^2 - 14.7 \text{ lb/in.}^2) \times 6.90 \times 10^4 \text{ dynes/cm}^2/\text{lb/in.}^2$

$$= 3.65 \times 10^5 \text{ dynes/cm}^2 , \text{ then}$$

$$Q = \frac{3.65 \times 10^5 \text{dynes-cm}^2 \times \left(1 + \frac{20 \text{ lb/in.}^2 - 14.7 \text{ lb/in.}^2}{2(14.7 \text{ lb/in.}^2)}\right)}{1.94 \times 10^6 \text{ g/cm}^4\text{-sec}}$$

and

$$Q = 0.222 \text{ cm}^3/\text{sec} = 0.013 \text{ liters/min} .$$

Table VIII. Gas-viscosity data.[a]

Gas	Temperature (°C)	Viscosity (micropoises)
Air	18	182.7
Carbon dioxide	20	148.0
Carbon monoxide	21.7	175.3
Chlorine	20	132.7
Ethane	17.2	90.1
Ethylene	20	100.8
Helium	20	194.1
Hydrogen	20.7	87.6
Hydrogen chloride	18	142.6
Hydrogen sulfide	17	124.1
Methane	20	198.7
Nitric oxide	20	187.6
Nitrogen	27.4	178.1
Nitrous oxide	26.9	148.8
Oxygen	19.1	201.8
Propane	17.9	79.5
Sulfur dioxide	20.5	125.4
Xenon	20	226.0

[a]Values selected from Reference 63.

Orifice meters are available to everyone with even the most rudimentary laboratory equipment. They can be constructed and easily calibrated against a wet test meter or soap-bubble meter. Care must be exercised not to plug the orifice with particles or to exceed the maximum pressure and force the manometer indicating oil out of the U-tube. These meters are useful but have the disadvantage of suffering a high pressure loss through each orifice. Such loss varies from 40 to 90% of the static pressure drop as the orifice-to-pipe diameter changes from 0.8 to 0.3.[30]

Critical Orifices

Critical orifices have been used extensively for maintaining and controlling gas streams at predetermined constant flow rates.[64-68] Sections of glass tubing, capillary tubing,[69] and hypodermic needles[67,70-73] have all been used to achieve a remarkably uniform flow rate.

An orifice as shown in Figure 20 is said to be critical when the ratio of the downstream pressure, P_2, to the upstream pressure, P_1, produces a sonic velocity at the orifice gas exit. For air, this condition is met when P_2 is less than 0.53 P_1 and the ratio of the upstream cross-sectional area, A_1, to the orifice area, A_2, is greater than 25.[1,30,74]

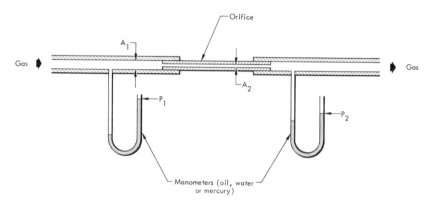

Figure 20. Sketch of a typical critical orifice meter. Sonic velocity is achieved when the downstream pressure, P_2, is less than 0.53 times the upstream pressure, P_1, and the ratio of A_1 to A_2 is greater than 25.

The calculations for the maximum flow rate, Q_{max}, for gas are complex and are derived in Reference 1. For a perfect gas through rounded orifices and nozzles,

$$Q_{max} = C_D A_2 P_1 \left[\frac{g K_H M}{RT} \left(\frac{2}{K_H + 1} \right)^{(K_H+1)/(K_H-1)} \right]^{\frac{1}{2}}, \quad (38)$$

C_D = discharge coefficient (no dimensions),

A_2 = cross-sectional area (ft²),

P_1 = upstream pressure (lb/ft²),

g = acceleration due to gravity (32.1740 ft/sec²),

K_H = ratio of the specific heat at constant pressure to the specific heat at constant volume,

M = molecular weight (lb/mole),

R = molar gas constant (1546 ft-lb/mole-°F), and

T = absolute temperature (°R).

For air, Equation 38 reduces to the more workable expression,[71]

$$Q_{max} = \frac{0.388 \ CA_2 P_1}{T^{\frac{1}{2}}}, \qquad (39)$$

where Q_{max} is measured in g/sec, A_2 in cm², P_1 in g/cm², and T in °K.

EXAMPLE 6. What is the theoretical maximum flow rate in grams per second and liters per minute when a vaccuum pump draws air through a 0.0125-inch-i.d. capillary tube? Assume that the discharge coefficient is unity, that the room temperature is 25°C, and that the atmospheric pressure is 760 mm Hg.

$$Q = \frac{0.388 \times 76 \ cm \times 13.6 \ g/cm^3 \times 3.14 \times (0.00625 \ in. \times 2.54 \ cm/in.)^2}{298°K^{\frac{1}{2}}},$$

$$Q = 1.83 \times 10^{-2} \ g/sec,$$

$$Q = \frac{1.83 \times 10^{-2} \ g/sec \times 22.4 \ liters/mole \times 298°K \times 60 \ sec/min)}{29.0 \ g/mole \times 273°K},$$

$$Q = 0.928 \ liters/min.$$

EXAMPLE 7. If the upstream and downstream pressures are 3.0 and 1.4 atm respectively for a 1-mm² orifice, does the gas flow reach sonic velocity at the orifice? If so, what is the flow in g/sec? The discharge coefficient is 0.85 and the temperature is 100°C.

Critical flow exists if $P_2 < 0.53 \ P_1$ or if $1.4 < 0.53 \times 3.0$.
Since $1.40 < 1.59$, the orifice is critical.

$$Q = \frac{0.388 \times 0.85 \times (1 \times 10^{-2} \ cm^2) \times 3.0 \ atm \times 1033 \ g/cm^2/atm)}{373°K^{\frac{1}{2}}},$$

$$Q = 0.53 \ g/sec.$$

Although Equation 39 would lead one to believe that the length of the orifice has no effect on the existing gas flow rate, this is not the case in practice. Table IX shows data on flow-rate variance with length under the same laboratory conditions, but the exact relationship is uncertain.

Table IX. Flow rate as a function of needle gage and length.[a]

Needle gage	Flow rate (in liters/min) for a needle length of:									
	3.5 in.	3.0 in.	2.5 in.	2.0 in.	1.5 in.	1.25 in.	1.0 in.	0.75 in.	0.625 in.	0.5 in.
13	12.2(2)									
15	8.9(1)									
17				5.89(1)						
18				3.77(3)	4.1(3)		4.45(2)			
19		2.15(7)		2.37(5)	2.43(5)	2.58(3)				
20			1.67(5)	1.75(1)	1.83(3)	1.97(1)	1.97(2)			
21				1.23(2)	1.32(3)	1.38(2)	1.47(3)			
22		0.59(15)		0.68(4)	0.80(3)	0.76(6)	0.89(3)			
23				0.42(2)	0.49(4)	0.54(2)	0.54(6)	0.69(6)	0.61(5)	0.63(5)
24					0.29(3)	0.40(3)	0.42(5)	0.45(4)	0.50(5)	0.51(4)
25				0.19(5)			0.26(4)	0.31(3)	0.31(6)	0.34(9)

[a]Measured at 630 mm Hg. Each flow rate is the mean for 12 needles. The values in parentheses are the relative standard deviations. Data taken from Reference 67.

Critical orifices have the advantages of being inexpensive, convenient, and easy to operate. They are ideal for sampling or mixing gas streams at a single constant rate for long periods if reasonable care is taken to protect the orifice from debris or wear. By using glass fibers, membrane filters, or glass-wool plugs placed upstream from the orifice,[67] reasonable accuracies ($\pm$3% for hypodermic needles[71]) can be maintained.

The disadvantages are few but significant. Only one critical flow rate is possible from each orifice, and the pressure differential required to maintain it is relatively high. Each orifice must be individually calibrated for even reasonable accuracy since the flow rate calculated from the pressure, temperature, and cross-sectional area can differ from the experimental flow rate by as much as 300%.[71]

Porous Plugs

A system regulating gas flows of a fraction of a milliliter per minute was devised by Saltzman and Gilbert[75] and later improved by Avera.[76] This device is the porous, packed, or asbestos-plug flowmeter, which has no moving parts, can be built from basic materials in the laboratory, and can regulate flows down to 0.01 ml/min. This flowmeter is particularly useful in producing gas mixtures in the parts-per-million range without double dilution or the use of excessive volumes of gas for a single dilution. Ethylene oxide, chlorine, chlorine dioxide, ammonia, phosgene,[77] nitrogen dioxide (0.5%),[78] nitric oxide (1%),[75] and radioactive sulfur dioxide[79] are examples of gases which have been metered through such devices. Asbestos-plug flowmeters provide steady concentration, maintained for many hours. They are compact and inexpensive, and rapid changes in concentration can be made.

A porous plug is shown in Figure 21. The gas of interest passes into the side arm of a 1–4-mm bore of a three-way capillary stopcock, where it is split into two gas streams. The bulk of the gas proceeds through a droplet trap and escapes into a graduated vessel containing some liquid. The balance of the stream proceeds through the packed arm of the stopcock, which contains medium-length acid-washed asbestos fibers of the type used in Gooch crucibles.[78] The stopcock, which is always maintained in the same position, is filled by tamping the fibers with a blunt piece of wire of appropriate diameter from both sides of the "T." The amount of tamping required will depend on the flow rates desired. A more tightly packed stopcock will yield a proportionally lower flow rate through it. The asbestos must be kept scrupulously free from grease or moisture, and it should be dried and cleaned with trichloroethylene or chloroform before tamping. The stopcock plug should be lightly coated with fluorocarbon or fluorosilicon grease to prevent gas leaks, but excess lubricant must be kept out the bore.

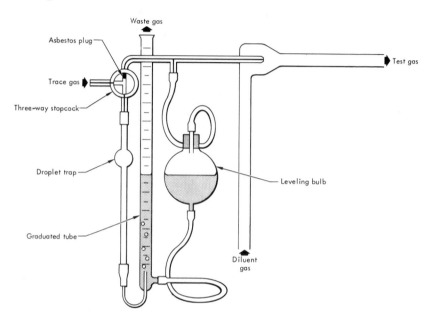

Figure 21. Sketch of a typical porous-plug flowmeter. The flow rate is adjusted by changing the height of the leveling bulb.

The flow rate is proportional to the pressure drop across the asbestos plug, and the upstream pressure is maintained by discharging the excess gas into a liquid column of known height. By varying the liquid height between the surface and the point of gas admission, a linear calibration plot of height versus flow rate can be constructed.

Losses out of the waste-gas outlet can be minimized if low or microflow needle valves are employed. If appreciable downstream pressures are encountered, a leveling bulb can be added to the system as shown to automatically compensate for either positive or negative output pressures.[76] By raising or lowering the bulb, the flow rate can be altered without adding water to the system.

The leveling bulb is connected between the outlet and the graduated vessel with flexible tubing, and it can be raised and lowered freely. The area of the bulb should be 80 to 100 times the area of the gas-escape vessel so that it will change only a small amount compared to the receiving vessel if the downstream pressure changes occur.[76]

The outlet bore of the flowmeter should be as small as possible, and capillary stopcocks are preferred. The small bore reduces the time to reach equilibrium and is especially important at low flow rates. It is also best to employ a large-diameter waste tube so that the pressure drop is negligible even at the higher waste-escape flow rates.[77] A droplet trap is provided in case the gas supply is disconnected too rapidly, for the inertia of the waste liquid could rise and wet the plug, rendering it useless.

Calibration is accomplished by timing the rate of movement of a water or oil drop in a 1.0–0.1-ml graduated volumetric pipet attached to the delivery end of the capillary stopcock.[18]

Controlled Leaks and Restrictors

Any material which offers resistance to gas flow can be used to control the flow rate. Just as tamped asbestos, with its convolutions and tortuous channels, inhibits the progress of a gaseous material, so also does a wide variety of other materials. For example, a flattened copper tube containing a stainless-steel wire will allow a small but perceptible and reproducible amount of gas to flow.[61]

The most widely used and commercially available restrictors are constructed from porous metal. A powdered metal alloy is compressed and cold-welded in an appropriate coupling. The particle size of the powder determines the pore openings and hence the flow rate. Gas flows when a pressure differential exists between the inlet and the outlet. This occurs as a result of either pressure on the inlet or a vacuum on the outlet.[80,81]

Restrictors and controlled leaks find wide use in regulating carrier-gas flows in gas chromatographs and they can perform the triple functions of gas-flow regulation, filtration, and surge dampening. Small flows on the order of 10^{-3} to 10^{-8} ml/sec at specified pressure differentials are said to be controlled leaks, while those from 10^{-3} to 10^{-2} ml/sec are said to be flow restrictors.[82] They are usually constructed from stainless steel, but others made of gold, silver, Monel, nickel, Inconel, and various alloys are available. Several shapes and sizes can be obtained, and a few are shown in Figure 22.

Standard flow tolerances as low as ±1% are also available, but uniform permeability is usually ±5 to 10%. The flow rate, of course, varies with the porosity, and a typical performance chart for a 1/16-inch element is shown in Figure 23.

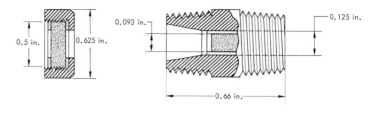

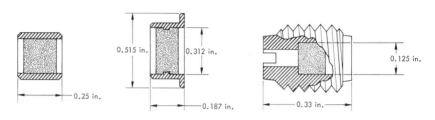

Figure 22. Cross sections of five controlled leaks and restrictors. (Taken from Reference 82.)

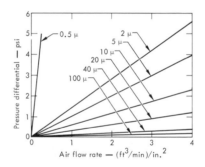

Figure 23. Pressure differential versus the flow rate of air for seven restrictor porosities. The data is for a 2/16-in. stainless-steel controlled leak. (Taken from Reference 82.)

Velocity Meters

There are a number of alternate techniques for measuring the velocity or flow rate of a gas past a mechanical or electric sensing point. These include thermal gradients, rotating- and deflecting-vane flowmeters, and drag-body and other mass flowmeters of various types. Their flow rates cover almost the entire spectrum from less than 0.01 cc/min to 1000 ft³/min. They must all be calibrated against a primary standard, for absolute flow rates are not usually available from calculations.

Thermal Transfer Methods

A large number of air velocity and flow meters depend on the rate of cooling or heat transfer from a heated probe. Among them are heated wires, thermocouples, and thermistors.

The heated- or hot-wire flowmeter consists of a thin, heated wire or film flow transducer placed rigidly in the gas stream to be measured. The sensor is electrically heated above ambient temperature and the amount of heat loss from the wire is a function of the gas velocity and flow rate, or more specifically, mass flow rate. The mass flow rate can be represented by

$$Q_m = \rho A \bar{u} \quad , \tag{40}$$

where

Q_m = mass flow (g/sec),

ρ = gas density (g/cm³),

A = cross-sectional area of the channel (cm²), and

$\bar{u}$ = velocity of the gas (cm/sec).

If A is kept constant, then Q_m is directly proportional to the density-velocity product (*i.e.*, the momentum per unit area of the gas stream). Hence, if the gas behaves ideally with pressure and temperature variations, the true flow rate should be automatically compensated for through a corresponding heat-loss change. As the temperature of the wire changes, its resistance changes and this is usually measured with a bridge circuit. Sensors are generally wires of tungsten, platinum, or platinum alloy, but thin films of gold supported by a quartz rod have been employed.[83,84] Since any temperature change will normally cause a variation in the indicated flow rate, the usual practice is to employ two hot-wire sensors. One wire is the actual sensing wire, while the other is a reference and each is used as an element in a four-element bridge circuit. The circuit maintains a fixed current ratio in the two sensors. A feedback amplifier controls the currents, maintaining a fixed voltage ratio across the two sensors and thereby keeping a constant resistance ratio even as the temperatures vary.[85] Further information on the fundamental mathematical expressions dealing with rates of heat loss for laminar and turbulent flow can be found in Owen and Pankhurst[31] and Arya and Plate.[86] Two common types of transducers are shown schematically in Figure 24. Basically, they both employ a measuring sensor and some type of shielded reference sensor. Inlet screens are sometimes used to straighten the flow and trap large particles.[87]

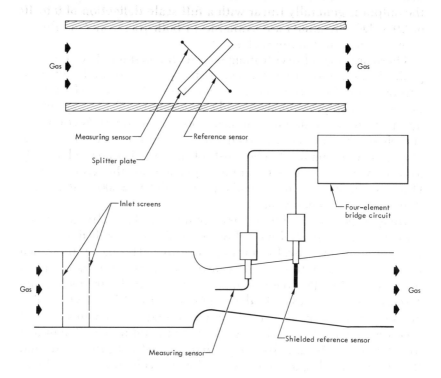

Figure 24. Cross-sections of two types of temperature-compensated gas-flow transducers.

This type of system has several advantages over other types of flow-measuring devices, especially the variable-area flowmeters. Since the unit generates a DC voltage proportional only to the mass flow rate of the gas, it is almost unaffected by pressure and temperature changes. These instruments offer an uncommonly large range of flow rates, and the range in gas is generally from 0.1 ml/min to 300 ft³/min.[88] The probes can also measure velocity, turbulence, and temperature as well as the mass flow rate in gases as well as liquids.

Readout is in actual flow units, and a flow-indicator calibration chart is usually unnecessary. Accuracies of ±0.5% with a repeatability of ±0.1% are common, and accuracies of ±0.2% and repeatabilities of ±0.01% full scale have been reported.[85] Accuracies of ±2% are obtainable even with temperature fluctuations of

±30° C and pressure changes of ⅓ to 3 atmospheres in air on some instruments.[87] Response time is on the order of milliseconds and the output is generally linear with a full scale deflection of 0 to 10 or 20 V DC. Readouts are available in both linear and nonlinear output signals and meter scales.

There are several disadvantages to such a system. The presence of the heated wires makes these instruments unsuitable for measuring flows of reactive and corrosive gases. They also should not be used in explosive or flammable atmospheres.[32] Foreign matter and particulate contamination cause erratic meter deflection, but self-cleaning circuits are available to minimize the effects of stream contaminants.[85] The cost of many of these electronic mass-flow meters makes them too expensive for the average user. However, there are some available for $150 to $300, but usually their cost will exceed $1000.

Heated-thermistor flowmeters operate on basically the same principle as the heated-wire flowmeter, for they both depend on the rate of heat removal from a fixed sensor. The basic difference is that cooling of the sensor causes an increase rather than a decrease in the effective resistance of the heated-wire technique. Thermistors have several advantages over the heated wire. The measuring probe can be made much stronger mechanically and less sensitive to shock. The resistance-temperature coefficient of a thermistor is substantially larger than that of a heated wire and therefore yields higher sensitivities for the same mass flow of gas. They need to be calibrated less frequently and are more useful in dusty atmospheres.[89]

As with the heated-wire type, probes are stationed in the gas stream. One thermistor is self-heated above ambient temperature (usually about 60–70°C) and measures the heat loss. The other is passive and performs the temperature-compensation function. Output scales are normally available in nonlinear or the more expensive linear readouts. Flow rates can range from less than 1 ml/min to over 1000 ft³/min with accuracies of ±1% and repeatabilities on the order of ±0.1%. Atmospheric pressure changes of ±50% in a temperature range of 12–41° C do not significantly change the calibration.[96]

Heated thermocouples also operate under the usual mass-flow conditions and need no correction over a wide range of temperatures and pressures. The output is linear (within 1% full scale), and no electronic curve straightening is required. Corrections over a static pressure range of 1.5–265 psi and between 0 and 40°C are not required. Full-scale ranges are from 0.5 cm³/min to 200 ft³/min, and flow rates as low as 0.01 ml/min could be detected with special electronics such as a self-balancing potentiometer.[91] Accuracies of ±2% are routine and repeatability is better than ±1%. They can be obtained commercially as single units or as dual metering units for producing gas mixtures.[92]

Mechanical Methods

Among the most common mechanically activated gas-flow indicators are the rotating- and deflecting-vane anemometer. Both types of instruments are used to measure the gas velocity at a certain position across a duct or pipe. They normally find the most use in industrial ventilation applications since they are portable and do not depend on any external power source. The calibration of such instruments must be periodically checked in an atmosphere which is uniform, predictable, and free of turbulence.[93]

The rotating-vane anemometer consists of a revolution counter activated by a revolving propeller. The dial normally reads in linear feet, which, when divided by the time interval of the measurement, gives the average gas velocity. The range of such instruments is limited and is generally from 200–2000 ft/min. It should not be used in dusty or corrosive atmospheres or temperatures or pressures far from room conditions.[30]

The deflecting-vane anemometers are also primarily used in industrial ventilation work and offer only a spot check of air velocity. They are available with up to four velocity ranges, have an effective range from 50–24,000 ft/min,[30] and are activated by the force of the gas against a spring-loaded swinging vane. Again, dust and corrosive gases seriously affect the indicated velocity, and care must be exercised to use them only in clean environments.

Electromechanical Methods

The drag-body flowmeter is a good example of the electromechanical method of flow-rate measurement, and it is shown schematically in Figure 25. As the flow commences, the gas exerts a force on the drag disc. The force is transmitted along the lever arm to the strain-gauge transducer. The electrical output is nonlinear but can be accurate to ±0.5% and repeatable to ±0.1%. Long-term repeatability has proven to be better than ±1% over years of service.[94]

The drag-body flowmeter has long been used for liquids but has not yet been fully exploited for gases. The range of single flow transducers is normally only 10 to 1, with the smallest measurable flow rate in the neighborhood of 1 liter/min. It does, however,

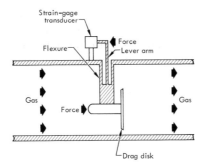

Figure 25. Idealized cross section of a
drag-body flowmeter.

have the advantages of no rotating or wearing parts, and if the drag
disc is sufficiently inert it is not affected by corrosive gases. It is
also able to operate over wide temperature ranges (−54° to 150°C)
and at pressures up to 5000 psi.[95]

There are other electromechanical devices available (*e.g.,* the
turbine flowmeter[35]), but these are designed primarily for liquid
rather than gaseous flow.

Miscellaneous Devices

A great many other devices are used for flow-rate determination.
Among them are instruments which depend on pressure, ioniza-
tion,[96] heated and Kata thermometers, and magnetic suscepti-
bilities.

Chapter 4

Static Systems for
Producing Gas Mixtures

The static or batch system is commonly used for producing standard gas and vapor mixtures. This involves the introduction of a known weight or volume of contaminant into a container of fixed dimensions. Nonrigid containers holding metered volumes of gases are also used. Static devices may be used at any desirable pressure, but laboratory applications are generally limited to systems at atmospheric pressure or slightly below. Static systems are usually employed when comparatively small volumes are required, and they are used extensively for instrument calibration and the production of gas-phase standards for gas chromatography, mass spectrometry, and infrared spectrophotometry.

SYSTEMS AT ATMOSPHERIC PRESSURE

Single Rigid Chambers

One of the most convenient methods of making an analytical gas standard is based on admitting a predetermined amount of solvent or gas into a single rigid vessel of known dimensions as shown in Figure 26. The contaminant is vaporized if necessary, mixed with the diluent gas, and sampled. Another inlet provides for replacement gas in order to keep the system at atmospheric pressure. A wide variety of chamber sizes has been used—from small syringes,[97,99] polyethylene bottles,[100,101] and flasks[102] to large test chambers in the cubic-meter range[103-105] and even large rooms.[106,107] The most usual size, however, is on the order of 20 to 40 liters.[100,108-110] This allows for the removal of enough useful gas without causing excessive dilution by the replacement gas.

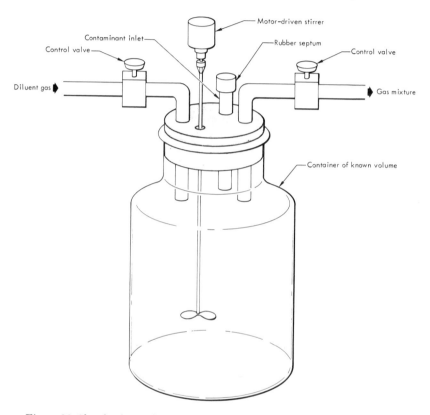

Figure 26. Sketch of a rigid static system for producing gas and vapor mixtures.

The materials chosen for construction should be such that the walls are smooth and do not cause excessive adsorption or reaction. Glass bottles are generally used, but phenolic,[101] epoxy,[105] Teflon, stainless steel,[104,111] and polyvinyl chloride[112] materials have also been used.

The volume of the system must be easily determined no matter what the size, shape, or material chosen for construction. The volume is found by direct measurement of the chamber boundaries or by filling the chamber with water and determining the size volumetrically. An alternative method is to evacuate the vessel and meter the diluent gas into it through a wet test meter.

Sample Introduction

Introduction of the contaminant gas or liquid into the calibration system can be accomplished in a number of ways. Some current methods are summarized in Table X and shown in Figure 27. One of the best devices is a glass syringe. Syringes for liquids (Figure 27A) in the microliter range are reported to have accuracies and reproducibilities of ±1%. Gas-tight syringes (Figure 27B) fitted with Teflon-tipped plungers in the 0.05–50-ml volume range may be used for both gases and liquids. Huge "super syringes" (1.5-liter capacity) and Teflon syringes for reactive materials are also commercially available. Ground-glass syringes should be avoided because of leakage, especially when dispensing small quantities of liquids.

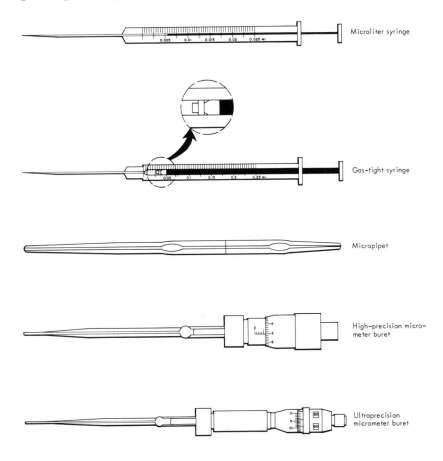

Figure 27. Sketches of five kinds of devices for injecting gases and liquids.

Table X. Characteristics of solvent and gas injectors.

Injector	Material injected	Plunger construction	Capacity	Accuracy at capacity[a]
Microliter syringe	Liquid	Wire	1 to 5 μl	±2%[113]
Microliter syringe	Liquid	Wire	5 to 500 μl	±1%[113]
Gas-tight syringe	Liquid, gas	Teflon-tipped	0.05 to 2.5 ml	±1%[113]
Gas-tight syringe	Liquid, gas	Teflon-tipped	5.0 to 50 ml	±1%[113]
"Super" syringe	Liquid, gas	Teflon-coated aluminum	0.5 to 1.5 liters	—
Micropipet	Liquid	Air	2 to 4 μl	±1.8%[114]
Micropipet	Liquid	Air	5 to 25 μl	±0.5%[114]
Micropipet	Liquid	Air	35 to 150 μl	±0.3%[114]
Micrometer buret (high-precision)	Liquid	Teflon	0.20 to 2.0 ml	±0.5%[115]
Micrometer buret (ultraprecision)	Liquid	Glass	0.25 to 2.5 ml	±0.02 to 0.04%[115]
Volumetric pipet	Liquid	Air	0.5 to 200 ml	±1%

[a]Data taken as noted from References 113, 114, and 115.

There are several methods used to fill syringes with gases,[103,116,117] one of which is illustrated in Figure 28. Pure gas from a small lecture bottle flows slowly into a liquid reservoir through a section of rubber or polymer tubing. The valve is turned just enough to start the gas bubbling in the liquid. The syringe needle pierces the tubing, and after several flushes the syringe is filled and withdrawn. Small lecture bottles of pure (usually 99+%) gases are available commercially for a few dollars.[118,119]

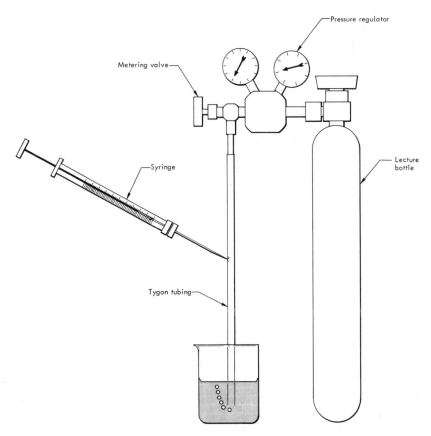

Figure 28. Setup for filling a syringe with a gas.

The contaminant gas or liquid is usually injected into the vessel through a soft material which allows the syringe needle to penetrate and be withdrawn without significant leakage. Rubber stoppers, serum caps,[120] and various rubberized septums[109] have been used for this purpose. The syringe should be depressed smoothly and evenly when injecting into the calibration vessel only once. If the dead volume in the needle is injected, it could cause high readings, especially when microliter quantities are being used. A slight vacuum in the sample container is sometimes needed to assist the contaminant into the container, especially when working with moderately-sized steel cylinders which have no internal mixing device.[121]

Measured volumes of liquids are also dispensed with micro- or lambda pipets (Figure 27C). They have the advantage of no dead volume, but unlike a syringe, which can dispense a wide range of volumes, a pipet yields only one measured solvent volume. Variable-volume precision liquid dispensers are available and are shown in Figures 27D and 27E. Micrometer syringes and burets have a reported accuracy of 0.5% and can dispense volumes up to 2 ml.[122] Ultraprecision micrometer syringes and burets made of glass and Teflon attain an accuracy of 0.02–0.04% when delivering volumes up to 2.5 ml. Variable-volume (0.030–3.000-ml) gas dispensers are not generally available but have been designed and can yield accuracies in the neighborhood of 0.2%.[123]

Gas Blenders

When the contaminant concentration of a mixture is relatively large (in the per cent range), gas burets are commonly used to measure, move, and mix the various gaseous components.[124-127] Figure 29 illustrates an example of this type. The gas buret, a vessel of known volume, moves measured volumes of gas to the main chamber by means of an advancing front of mercury or water.[128] Various volumes may be preselected by using calibrated scribe marks on the buret.[129,130] Volumetric burets are often used to measure these gas volumes, and this method has been used for years in Orsat gas analyzers. When extreme care is taken, certain types of gas blenders have reported blending accuracies of 0.01%,[131] but this is unusual.

Miscellaneous Volume Dispensers

Small volumes of gases can be swept over the test chamber with calibrated by-passes as shown in Figure 30. The main test chamber is evacuated, then the material of interest flows through and fills the by-pass. The stopcocks are then readjusted and the contaminant is swept into the main calibration vessel with the diluent gas.

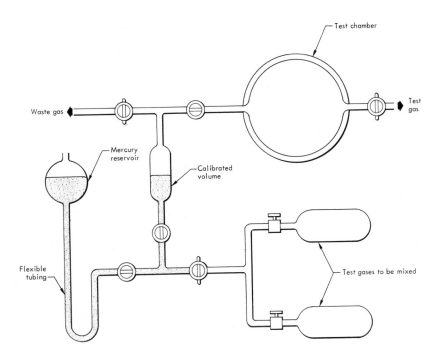

Figure 29. Setup for mixing measured volumes of gases via an advancing mercury or water front.

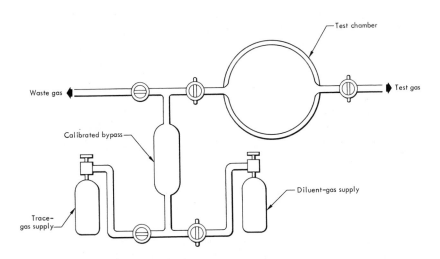

Figure 30. Setup for mixing measured volumes of gases with a calibrated bypass.

Liquids can be introduced into test chambers in small ampoules. The solvent is added to a tared ampoule, sealed with a flame, weighed, and added to the vessel. The ampoule can be broken either with a metal plunger[117] or by shaking it with another metal object in an unbreakable container.[100] The quantitative transfer and injection of small samples (0.001– 10 μmoles) of gases and vapors have been accomplished using closed glass tubes equipped with hemispheric break seals.[132]

The use of chemical reactions in preparing standard mixtures is especially important for some gases. Hydrogen cyanide, for example, is especially difficult to handle, but it can be handled more easily if small quantities are generated by reacting known quantities of potatassium cyanide in an excess of concentrated sulfuric acid (see Chapter 6). Nitrogen dioxide is similarly prepared from the decomposition of lead nitrate.

Mixing Devices

Once the sample has been added to the calibration vessel, means must be provided to mix the gas or evaporate the liquid and mix the vapors. Several of these methods are summarized in Figure 31. One of the most common and probably the best all-round method is the use of some type of fan or stirrer. For very large chambers which approach room size, an overhead circulation fan is sufficient.[105,133] Smaller systems in the 20–40-liter size use internal propellers driven by external motors of air stirrers. Small squirrel-cage motors placed inside the vessel have been used for mixtures below the explosive range.[109] For smaller systems on the order of 1 liter or so, a magnetic stirrer will suffice.[127]

Before mixing can occur, some source of heat is required to vaporize the higher boiling solvents. In large systems, the sample is simply evaporated on a hotplate inside the vessel. Volatilization with infrared lamps,[134] sandbaths,[105] small light bulbs,[133] and Nichrome wire[103] has also been used. These evaporation techniques are sometimes needed for volatilization of gases if they are admitted to the vessel dissolved in a liquid.[135]

If no stirrer is available, the liquid sample can be injected on absorbent paper, which increases the surface area and leads to faster evaporation. Foil strips, moved about by container inversion, will greatly increase the speed of volatilization.[100]

Concentration Calculations

The concentration by volume of a contaminant gas or vapor in a

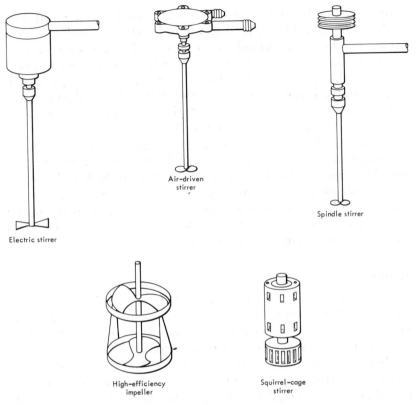

Air-driven
stirrer

Spindle stirrer

Electric stirrer

High-efficiency
impeller

Squirrel-cage
stirrer

Figure 31. Sketches of five devices for mixing gases and vapors in a rigid chamber.

gas mixture can be calculated either in per cent or in parts per million, depending on the magnitude of the concentrations desired. For a gas mixture in the ppm range, the calculation is

$$C = \frac{10^6 \, v_C}{v_D} , \qquad (41)$$

where v_C and v_D are the contaminant and diluent volumes respectively. If the concentration in per cent is desired, then

$$C = \frac{10^2 \, v_C}{v_D + v_C} . \qquad (42)$$

EXAMPLE 8. What is the concentration in parts per million when 10 ml of chlorine gas is added to a 5-gal container?

$$C = \frac{10^6 \times 10 \text{ ml}}{5.0 \text{ gal} \times 3785 \text{ ml/gal}} = 5.3 \times 10^2 \text{ ppm.}$$

EXAMPLE 9. What is the concentration in per cent when 800 ml of propane gas is added to a 40.0-liter container? Assume that no diluent air is lost when the sample is added.

$$C = \frac{10^2 \times 0.800 \text{ liters}}{40.0 \text{ liters} + 0.800 \text{ liters}} = 1.96\%.$$

If a liquid is added to a closed system, the resulting concentration, expressed in parts per million, can be calculated from the expression,

$$C = \frac{(22.4 \times 10^6) \times \dfrac{T}{273°K} \times \dfrac{760 \text{ mm}}{P} \times W}{VM} \qquad (43)$$

where

$$\begin{aligned}
C &= \text{concentration (ppm),}\\
W &= \text{weight (g),}\\
T &= \text{absolute temperature of system (°K),}\\
M &= \text{molecular weight (g/mole),}\\
P &= \text{pressure of the system (mm Hg), and}\\
V &= \text{volume of system (liters).}
\end{aligned}$$

At normal room temperature (25°C) and 1 atm, Equation 43 reduces to

$$C = \frac{(24.5 \times 10^6) \times W}{VM}. \qquad (44)$$

EXAMPLE 10. What is the concentration when 50 mg of acetone is added to a 20-liter container at 25°C and 760 mm Hg?

$$C = \frac{(24.5 \times 10^6) \times 0.05 \text{ g}}{20 \text{ liters} \times 58.1 \text{ g/mole}} = 1054 \text{ ppm.}$$

EXAMPLE 11. What is the weight in grams of carbon tetrachloride needed to achieve a concentration of 500 ppm in a 10-ft^3 chamber? The atmospheric pressure and temperature are 25°C and 745 mm Hg respectively.

$$W = \frac{CVM}{(22.4 \times 10^6) \times \dfrac{T}{273°K} \times \dfrac{760 \text{ mm}}{P}}$$

$$= \frac{500 \text{ ppm} \times 10 \text{ ft}^3 \times 28.3 \text{ liters/ft}^3 \times 153.8 \text{ g/mole}}{(22.4 \times 10^6) \times \dfrac{298°K}{273°K} \times \dfrac{760 \text{ mm}}{745 \text{ mm}}} = 0.872 \text{ g.}$$

More often, however, the volume of material needed is a more useful variable. If

$$W = \rho v_L , \tag{45}$$

where ρ is the density (g/ml) and v_L is the liquid volume (ml), then Equation 43 becomes

$$C = \frac{(22.4 \times 10^6) \times \rho v_L \times \dfrac{T}{273°K} \times \dfrac{760 \text{ mm}}{P}}{MV} . \tag{46}$$

EXAMPLE 12. What is the concentration when 200 μl of benzene is injected into a 5-gal bottle? The temperature and pressure are 18°C and 14 lb/in.² respectively.

$$C = \frac{22.4 \text{ liters/mole} \times 10^6 \times 0.880 \text{ g/ml} \times 0.200 \text{ ml} \times 291°K \times 14.7 \text{ lb/in.}^2}{78.1 \text{ g/mole} \times 5.00 \text{ gal} \times 3.78 \text{ liters/gal} \times 273°K \times 14.0 \text{ lb/in.}^2}$$

$$= 2990 \text{ ppm.}$$

EXAMPLE 13. What volume of ethanol must be vaporized in a 30-ft³ chamber to produce a concentration of 1000 ppm at 20°C and 750 mm Hg?

$$v_L = \frac{1000 \text{ ppm} \times 46.1 \text{ g/mole} \times 30.0 \text{ ft}^3 \times 28.3 \text{ liters/ft}^3 \times 273°K \times 750 \text{ mm Hg}}{0.789 \text{ g/ml} \times 22.4 \text{ liters/mole} \times 293°K \times 760 \text{ mm Hg} \times 10^6}$$

$$= 2.04 \text{ ml.}$$

Volume-Dilution Calculations

After the standard gas mixture is obtained, it is sampled or moved to a new container where the appropriate measurements are made. Removing the test material from the container usually requires the introduction of some type of make-up dilution gas. It is useful, therefore, to be able to calculate what error might be introduced when known volumes of a gas sample are removed and replaced with a diluent gas. If one assumes instantaneous and perfect mixing with the incoming dilution gas and representative sample removal at a constant rate, then the change in concentration, dC, as each increment of volume is removed is equal to the concentration, C, times the fraction of the volume withdrawn, dV[30]:

$$dC = \frac{CdV}{V} . \tag{47}$$

This integrates to

$$C = c_0 \, e^{-v_W/V} , \tag{48}$$

and taking logs yields

$$2.303 \times \log \frac{c_0}{C} = \frac{v_W}{V} , \tag{49}$$

where

C = resultant concentration,

c_0 = original concentration,

v_W = volume of sample withdrawn, and

V = chamber volume.

If some part of the withdrawn sample is used and then returned as part of the make-up gas, the situation is somewhat more complicated, but such calculations have been made by Buchberg and Wilson.[136,137]

The validity of Equation 49 has been checked experimentally. Stead and Taylor,[108] for example, sampled benzene, carbon monoxide, and mercury vapors at various flow rates in a 5-gallon jug and found close agreement between actual and theoretical concentrations. Silver,[136] using a 20,000-liter room and a flow rate of 3600 liters/min, found the actual concentration to be within ±3% of the expected theoretical values.

EXAMPLE 14. What is the theoretical concentration of CH_3Br left in a 20-liter container after 10 liters of the gas mixture have been continuously removed and replaced with a diluent gas? The initial concentration is 500 ppm.

$$(2.3 \times \log 500) - (2.3 \times \log C) = \frac{10}{20}$$

$$C = 303 \text{ ppm}$$

EXAMPLE 15. How many chamber volumes are required to purge any given vessel to 1% of its original concentration? to 0.1% of the original concentration?

$$\frac{v_W}{V} = 2.30 \times \log \frac{100}{1} = 4.6 \text{ chamber volumes.}$$

$$\frac{v_W}{V} = 2.30 \times \log \frac{100}{0.1} = 6.9 \text{ chamber volumes.}$$

EXAMPLE 16. How long can a sample be withdrawn at 0.1 ft³/min before the concentration in a 1.0-m³ chamber is reduced by 5%?

$$v_W = 1.0 \text{ m}^3 \times 35.3 \text{ ft}^3/\text{m}^3 \times \left(2.3 \times \log \frac{100}{95}\right)$$

$$= 1.79 \text{ ft}^3,$$

$$\tau = 1.79 \text{ ft}^3 \times 0.1 \text{ ft}^3/\text{min} = 17.9 \text{ min}.$$

Sometimes it is desirable to sample from a rigid container without suffering make-up gas dilution or a significant internal pressure decrease. This is accomplished by attaching a deflated plastic bag to the dilution-gas inlet[30,139,140] as shown in Figure 32. As the mixture is sampled, dilution air fills the plastic bag as the mixture is displaced. Care must be taken, however, in selecting a bag which does not adsorb appreciable quantities of the material under study (see the section on nonrigid containers).

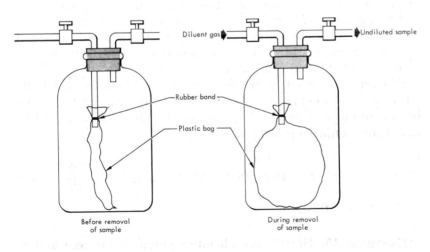

Before removal of sample

During removal of sample

Diluent gas

Undiluted sample

Rubber band

Plastic bag

Figure 32. Setup for removing a test gas from a rigid static system without causing sample dilution.

Discussion

The greatest advantage of the rigid static system is its simplicity of design. All of its components consist of readily available laboratory equipment which is relatively inexpensive and easy to operate. Accuracies of ±5% are rountinely obtainable in the ppm range if a few basic precautionary measures are undertaken.

The accuracy of the concentration produced from rigid containers generally depends on a knowledge of three major parameters: the contaminant purity, the volume of the system, and the volume of liquid or gas dispersed in the vessel. The other variables of molecular weight and gas density are available in the literature. Room temperature and pressure can be measured accurately with standard laboratory equipment.

Contaminant purity is usually specified by the manufacturer, but if doubt exists, liquids can be checked by distillation, refractive-index, or density determinations. Gas and liquid purities can be checked by a gas chromatograph if one is available.

If the injected volume of an ideal pure gas is known to within ±2%, the chamber volume to within 1%, and the gas purity to ±1%, the expected concentration produced is known to within ±3%. Even if great care is taken and all the proper correction factors are applied for nonideality, gas purities, and wall adsorption or reactions, accuracies of better than 1% are usually difficult to achieve in the ppm range. Mixtures in the per cent range, however, can be made more accurately[131] since the volumes of the contaminant gas can be measured more closely than 1%.

The disadvantages of a static system are numerous, but none is sufficiently critical to rule it out as a valid experimental technique. One of the main disadvantages is adsorption and reaction on the container walls.[141,142] Adsorption losses of 50% have been observed,[77] and particular care must be taken when low concentrations of strong oxidizing and reducing agents and polymerizable materials are prepared. Materials such as ozone, nitrogen dioxide, hydrogen fluoride, nitrated compounds, and styrene monomer are a few examples of such compounds. Adsorption losses can be reduced somewhat by increasing the size of the chamber, which decreases the surface-to-volume ratio, but even in large chambers (156 m³) the concentration of sulfur dioxide can decrease significantly after 2 hours.[143] Enlarging the chamber also makes it possible to sample larger volumes with less dilution, but then it takes correspondingly longer to flush the chamber between individually produced concentrations.

Static chambers are occasionally subject to implosion or explosion. Sometimes it is necessary to withdraw some of the chamber volume and work with a partial vacuum in a glass container if a large amount of contaminant is to be introduced.[140,144] Glass containers have been known to implode if there are weaknesses in the boundary wall. Vessel explosion can occur when working with concentrations above the lower explosive limit, and if a potentially dangerous situation might occur, the chamber can be surrounded with another nonbreakable vessel to prevent the spread of glass fragments. Van Sandt, for example, routinely encloses his 40-liter bottles within steel containers with a wire-mesh top.[109]

Rigid Chambers in Series

When laboratory space is at a premium, the use of relatively small containers to obtain large volumes of test gas at an almost constant concentration is still possible. This can be accomplished by connecting vessels in series as shown in Figure 33. Here, each container is filled with the desired concentration of contaminant and connected in series with some type of nonreactive tubing, usually glass. As the sample is withdrawn from the last container, dilution air enters the first vessel and dilutes the gas or vapor sample. The diluted gases then move to the second flask and again dilute the test mixture, but to a smaller degree. By adding more containers, large volumes can be withdrawn without seriously decreasing the expected concentration. For example, 2.5 times the final vessel's volume can be withdrawn from a five-container system before the residual concentration iis reduced to 90% of its initial value.[145]

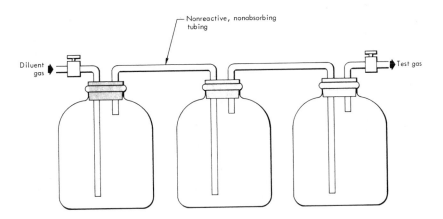

Figure 33. Sketch of rigid chambers connected in series.

Chamber materials, mixing devices, and evaporation methods can be any of the types discussed for single rigid containers. Gases and liquids are added with gas-tight syringes, microburets, or ultramicropipets, depending on the accuracy and concentration desired.

The concentrations emerging from each individual vessel are obtained from Equation 50. When the vessels are connected in series, the residual concentration in the final nth container, assuming perfect and instantaneous mixing, is calculated from the expression

$$c_n = c_0 \left[1 + \frac{1}{1!} \left(\frac{v_W}{V} \right) + \frac{1}{2!} \left(\frac{v_W}{V} \right)^2 \right.$$

$$\left. + \cdots + \frac{1}{(n-1)!} \left(\frac{v_W}{V} \right)^{n-1} \right] e^{-v_W/V}, \quad (50)$$

where

c_n = concentration of the nth vessel after the removal of v_W,

c_0 = initial concentration of all vessels,

V = total vessel volume,

v_W = volume of material withdrawn from the system, and

n = number of containers.

EXAMPLE 17. What is the theoretical concentration of methylene chloride left in a two- and a four-bottle system (each bottle holds 20 liters) after 40 liters have been withdrawn? The initial concentration is 1000 ppm.

$$C_2 = (1000 \text{ ppm}) \left[1 + \left(\frac{40}{20} \right) \right] e^{-40/20} = 406 \text{ ppm}.$$

$$C_4 = (1000 \text{ ppm}) \left[1 + \left(\frac{40}{20} \right) + \frac{1}{2} \left(\frac{40}{20} \right)^2 + \frac{1}{6} \left(\frac{40}{20} \right)^3 \right] e^{-40/20}$$

$$= 857 \text{ ppm}.$$

Table XI gives some of the dilution calculations up to a 10-bottle system. Note how the addition of each container greatly increases the sample volume produced before a given minimum concentration is reached. Equation 50 has been experimentally checked several times[109,111] and found to be valid after removal of up to 200% of the container volume.

Table XI. Residual concentrations present in series-connected vessels after the removal of a volume, v_W.

Volume withdrawn, $\left(\dfrac{v_W}{V}\right)100$	Residual concentration (in per cent) in the:						
	First vessel	Second vessel	Third vessel	Fourth vessel	Fifth vessel	Eighth vessel	Tenth vessel
0	100.00	100.00	100.00	100.00	100.00	100.00	100.00
10	90.48	99.53	99.98	100.00	100.00	100.00	100.00
20	81.87	98.25	99.89	99.99	100.00	100.00	100.00
40	67.03	93.84	99.21	99.92	99.99	100.00	100.00
60	54.88	87.81	97.69	99.66	99.96	100.00	100.00
80	44.93	80.88	95.26	99.09	99.86	100.00	100.00
100	36.79	73.58	91.97	98.10	99.63	100.00	100.00
125	28.65	64.46	86.85	96.17	99.09	100.00	100.00
150	22.31	55.78	80.88	93.44	98.14	99.98	100.00
175	17.38	47.79	74.40	89.92	96.71	99.95	100.00
200	13.53	40.60	67.67	85.71	94.73	99.89	100.00
250	8.21	28.73	54.38	75.76	89.12	99.58	99.97
300	4.98	19.91	42.32	64.72	81.53	98.81	99.89
350	3.02	13.59	32.08	53.66	72.54	97.33	99.67
400	1.83	9.16	23.81	43.35	62.88	94.89	99.19
450	1.11	6.11	17.36	34.23	53.21	91.34	98.29
500	0.674	4.04	12.47	26.50	44.05	86.66	96.82
550	0.409	2.66	8.84	20.17	35.75	80.95	94.62
600	0.248	1.74	6.20	15.12	28.51	74.40	91.61
700	0.091	0.730	2.96	8.18	17.30	59.87	83.05
800	0.033	0.302	1.38	4.24	9.96	45.30	71.66
900	0.012	0.123	0.62	2.12	5.50	32.39	58.74
1000	0.005	0.050	0.28	1.03	2.93	22.02	45.79

Multiple-vessel arrangements generally have the same advantages and disadvantages as does a single-vessel system. The multiple-container system will produce large volumes if it conforms to the dilution equation. This system is still relatively simple to operate and maintain in comparison with some of its dynamic counterparts.

There is an additional disadvantage besides the usual ones of wall absorption and reaction and time-consuming flushing between individually prepared concentrations. Series systems usually require vast areas of bench space and hence become unwieldly for the small laboratory. Five 40-liter glass bottles with all the accompanying paraphernalia, for example, will generally require about 12 feet of laboratory table top.

Nonrigid Chambers

A valuable alternative to the single or series arrangement of rigid vessels is the nonrigid container, or more simply, the plastic bag. These containers allow the entire sample to be withdrawn without any troublesome volume dilution with replacement air. As the sample is removed from the bag, the boundaries of the bag conform to the remaining volume and the resulting internal pressure change is usually negligible. Plastic bags not only have wide appeal for use in the laboratory, but gas mixtures can be carried into the field and used for instrument calibration. Bags can also be filled with gas samples at remote sites and sent to the laboratory for a complete analysis.[146]

The flexible chamber has several advantages over the rigid static system. The plastic containers are usually orders of magnitude less expensive, require no air dilution during sampling, and are light, compact, and easily portable. However, plastic bags cannot be used indiscriminately. Diffusion through the walls and sample decomposition and adsorption on the container walls must be taken into account, especially when samples are to be stored for long periods of time.

The plastic bag consists of a sealed flexible-wall container which can be inflated to full volume without stretching the bag boundaries. There is usually some type of inlet port and closing off device. Bags are constructed from a wide variety of materials, but usually polymers of some type are the most useful. Mylar, Saran Wrap, Scotchpak, plastic sandwich bags,[147] and even football bladders[148] have been used. Some of the physical properties are summarized in Tables XII and XIII.

The materials used in bag construction are generally from 1 to 5 mils in thickness. This allows the wall boundaries to assume any shape as long as the bag is not filled to capacity and the bag pressure does not exceed atmospheric pressure. The polymer is either used along or is laminated to some other material, usually aluminum. This aluminizing apparently seals the pores and makes the walls less permeable to the sample gases.[145] At any rate, the inner layer should be impermeable to the gases and the outer layer should be impermeable to moisture.[149]

Table XII. Characteristics of some common polymeric films.

Generic or brand name	Polymeric material	Thickness (mils)	Reference in which use of film is described
Mylar	Polyester (no plasticizer)	0.002	110, 146, 149-154
Aluminized Mylar	Polyester	0.002	149, 152
Saran Wrap, type 12	Polyvinylidene chloride	0.002	149
Saran Wrap, type 5-517	Polyvinylidene chloride	0.002	155
Scotchpak, type 20A5	Polyester (no plasticizer)	0.002	149, 152
Aluminized Scotchpak, type 20A20	Polyester	0.002	149, 152
Kel-F	Polyfluorocarbon	0.005	155
Cellophane	Cellulose	0.0015	155
Polyethylene	Polyethylene	0.005	155
Flex-O-Glass	Polyvinyl chloride	0.004	155
Teflon	Polyfluorocarbon	0.0023	146, 155
Cellothene	Polyethylene between layers of cellophane[a]	0.002	155

[a]Not suitable.

These data represent only a few random examples in a rather extensive field. The specifications were taken from the manufacturers' product bulletins. It does not in any way constitute a product endorsement by the author or the U.S. Atomic Energy Commission.

Flexible containers either may be purchased commercially[157,158] or made in the laboratory. Large sheets of polymers can be purchased, cut to the desired size, and sealed with a hot iron. Mylar, for example, can be obtainnd from 100-ft rolls, and Mylar tape can be used to seal the plastic layers together with a household iron[151] or rotary heat sealers. Double sealing is sometimes needed to ensure that bags are indeed free from leaks.[110] Bag sizes of 1 liter,[159] 20 liters,[160] 40 liters (42 in. by 24 in.),[110] 60 to 70 liters (50 in. by 18 in.),[149] and 200 liters[150] have been used.

Table XIII. Properties of some plastic films.[a]

Kind of plastic film	Chemical resistance[b] to:					Physical properties			
	Strong acids	Strong alkalis	Ketones and esters	Chloro-hydro-carbons	Hydro-carbons	Sealing temperature (°F)	H_2O absorption [g/100 in.²]/hr]	H_2O diffusion [(g/100 in.²)/hr]	O_2 diffusion [(g/100 in.²)/24 hr]
Cellophane (plain)	P	P	P	E	E	Not sealable	High	High	—
Cellophane (coated)	P	P	P	E	F	200 to 350	High	0.2 to 1.0	Low
Cellulose diacetate	P	P	P	P	G	400 to 500	Low	10 to 40	3 to 6
Cellulose triacetate	P	P	P	P	G	Not sealable	Low	10	—
Cellulose acetatebutyrate	P	P	P	P	G	—	Low	60	—
Cellulose nitrate	G	F	P	F	F	Not sealable	Low	—	—
Ethyl cellulose	P	E	P	P	F	—	Low	10 to 50	—
Polyester[c]	E	E	E	E	E	490	Very low	1.8	5.7
Polyethylene	E	E	G	F	F	250 to 400	Very low	1.2 to 1.4	550
Polytetrafluoro-ethylene[d]	E	E	E	E	E	Not sealable	None	None	None
Styrene	G	E	P	G	G	250 to 300	0.04	6.2	213
Polyvinyl alcohol	P	P	E	E	E	300 to 400	30	10	—
Polyvinylidene chloride	E	G	F	F	E	285	Very low	0.2	0.6
Vinyl-chloride copolymers	G	E	P	F	G	200 to 400	Very low	1.0	50
Rigid polyvinyl chloride[e]	E	E	P	F	E	300 to 400	Very low	0.5	23
Vinyl chloride, GRS blend	G	G	P	E	G	270 to 350	Very low	7.0	—
Rubber hydrochloride[f]	G	G	F	F	E	225 to 350	Very low	0.5 to 15.0	2 to 400

[a] Data taken from Reference 156.

These data represent only a few random examples in a rather extensive field. It does not in any way constitute a product endorsement by the author or the U.S. Atomic Energy Commission.

[b] E - Excellent, G - Good, F - Fair, P - Poor.
[c] Includes Mylar, Videne, and Scotchpak.
[d] Teflon.
[e] Poor folding endurance.
[f] Limited shelf life.

Sample Introduction

Before any contaminant or diluent gas is added the bag is rolled as tightly as possible to minimize the dead volume. The component gases are normally metered into the bag and stopped just before the bag is completely full, as shown in Figure 34A. Figures 34B, 34C, and 34D show several methods of sample introduction. Gaseous contaminants are normally added either slowly into the filling airstream (Figure 34B) or directly into the bag through a rubber patch after it is filled (Figure 34C). Gas-tight, Teflon-tipped syringes are used for either gases or liquids. If liquids are to be injected, they should be vaporized if possible by the incoming air outside the bag rather than injected directly onto the container walls (Figure 34D). The bag opening can be closed with a stopcock, a pinch clamp, or a screw-type valve, and mixing is accomplished by kneading the bag for several minutes.

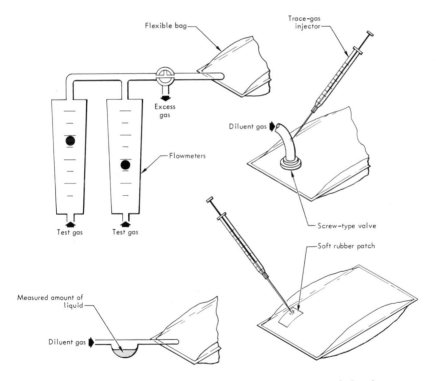

Figure 34. Four methods of introducing a sample into a nonrigid chamber.

Sample Decay

The initial concentration in a plastic bag will, with time, slowly decay toward a zero concentration. Some substances such as nitrogen dioxide and ozone will decay quickly, while other materials like sulfur dioxide and hydrocarbons[161] will exhibit less tendency to decrease in concentration. The decay of various materials in several types of flexible containers is shown in Table XIV,[149] and typical data are plotted in Figure 35[146] for sulfur dioxide. Sample losses are typically influenced by the bag material, the nature of the contaminant, the relative humidity, and transparency to radiation.[155] Examples of the effect of humidity are shown in Figure 36.[149] Note that higher humidity accelerates the decay process of a typical concentration. If there is doubt and the mixtures are to be stored for long periods of time, they should be checked before use to determine to what extent they have deteriorated.

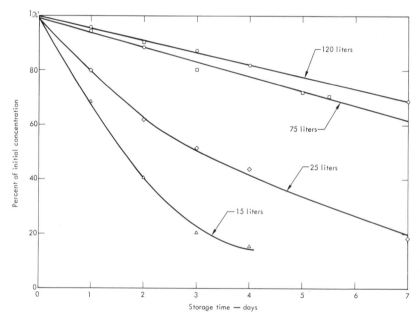

Figure 35. Concentration of SO_2 versus storage time in Mylar bags having capacities of 15, 25, 75, and 120 liters (initial SO_2 concentration = 1 ppm). (Taken from Reference 146.)

Sample decay can be lessened if the container is first preconditioned to the test substances. Preconditioning requires flushing out the bag several times with the test material. Some preconditioning cycles recommended require at least six refills, with at least one of them remaining in the bag overnight.[153] Although preconditioning is usually helpful, nitrogen dioxide, for example, decays at the same rate whether or not the preconditioning cycles have been used.

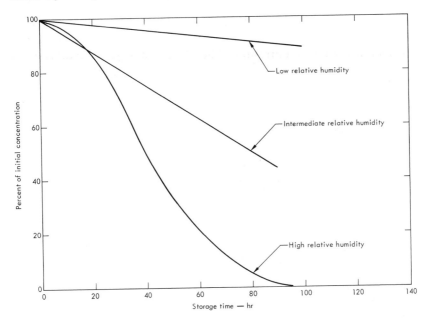

Figure 36. Concentration of NO_2 versus storage time in a 1-mm-thick aluminized Mylar bag at three different relative humidities (initial NO_2 concentration = 70 ppm, pressure = 760 mm Hg). (Taken from Reference 149.)

PRESSURIZED SYSTEMS

Pressurized systems are frequently used in the laboratory to produce large volumes of gas mixtures. Technically speaking, a pressurized system is a dynamic method since the usual procedure is to mix moving gas streams. However, the process of making and storing mixtures of gases in an appropriate cylinder is generally termed a static method of calibrated gas mixture production.

Pressurized systems are most easily obtained from commercial manufacturers at pressures of about 2000 psig. Higher pressures of 3500 to 6000 psig can be obtained on request for certain gases.[162] Pressurized gases and mixtures of gases are available commercially in a wide variety of sizes. They can be produced in sizes from large steel cylinders with volumes up to 200 ft³ to small aerosol cans which are good for volumes up to several liters.[163] They can, however, be produced in the laboratory if certain basic equipment is available. The three main types of pressurized systems are volumetric, manometric, and gravimetric. All three can be used efficiently to produce large volumes of standard gas mixtures from the low part-per-million range to the per cent range.

Table XIV. Evaluation of some polymeric films for storing various gases.[a]

Kind of film	Gage	Size (in.)	Gas components	Concentration[b] Initial	Concentration[b] Final	Storage time (hr)
Mylar	200	18 by 50	Butyraldehyde	55 (66)	50 (69)	24 (17)
			Ethylene	64	63	19
			2-Methyl pentane	—	—	—
			Benzene	76 (31)	81 (26)	18 (65)
			Acetone	60 (39)	62 (20)	18 (65)
			Nitrogen dioxide	52, 63, 64 (78)	41, 52, 44 (13)	18 (65)
			Sulfur dioxide	69, 58	68, 64	18
Aluminized Mylar	100	18 by 52	Nitrogen dioxide	54 (50)	47 (52)	22 (19)
			Sulfur dioxide	73 (70)	78 (77)	22 (19)
			2-Methyl pentane	71 (72)	73 (79)	22 (19)
Aluminized Mylar	100	18 by 52	Nitrogen dioxide	71, 49 (81)	18, 22 (18)	66 (24)
			Sulfur dioxide	129, 57 (82)	24, 30 (41)	66 (24)
			2-Methyl pentane	61 (65)	75 (67)	66 (18)
			Butyraldehyde	63 (79)	69 (77)	18 (24)
Saran Wrap	200	36 by 36	Nitrogen dioxide	64 (66)	39 (37)	19 (20)
			Benzene	72 (79)	76 (79)	19 (20)
			2-Methyl pentane	65	65	17
			Butyraldehyde	49	51	17
Scotchpak	200	36 by 32	Nitrogen dioxide	60, 66	30, 0	17, 23
			Acetone	56	78	17
			Benzene	70	74	17
			Sulfur dioxide	65	44	23
			2-Methyl pentane	60	64	23
			Butyraldehyde	49	50	23
Aluminized Scotchpak	200	36 by 34	Nitrogen dioxide	51, 76 (46)	0, 8 (6)	17 (18)
			Acetone	54	57	17
			Benzene	63	68	17
			Sulfur dioxide	83 (77)	73 (55)	17 (18)
			2-Methyl pentane	66	68	17
			Butyraldehyde	50	45	17

[a]Selected data taken from Reference 149.
These data represent only a few random examples in a rather extensive field. It does not in any way constitute a product endorsement by the author or the U.S. Atomic Energy Commission.
[b]The concentrations in parentheses correspond to the times in parentheses.

Volumetric Methods

Volumetric methods consist chiefly of metering known flows or volumes of gases and compressing them into a pressurized vessel. These methods are able to produce concentrations from the medium part-per-million range to the per cent range with accuracies in the neighborhood of ±1 to 10% depending on the technique chosen.

Figure 37 shows a typical volumetric system. Pure component gases from pressurized cylinders are metered through a flowmeter and compressed into another cylinder of suitable strength. The pure starting materials may have been previously diluted and may even be contained in vessels at atmospheric pressure or slightly above. Plastic bags and spirometers have been known to house the starting materials. If small volumes are required, then high-pressure, gas-tight syringes can be employed. Introduction of larger gas volumes can be done with calibrated gas volumes[130,164,165] much like the system shown in Figure 30. A chamber of known size is filled with the gas of interest and is subsequently swept into the source cylinder. The flowmeter can be almost any of the devices discussed in Chapter 3. Flowmeters and wet and dry test meters are the ones most frequently used. The compressor chosen is usually the diaphragm type in which the test gases do not come in contact with oil mists and other contaminants. Gases are usually

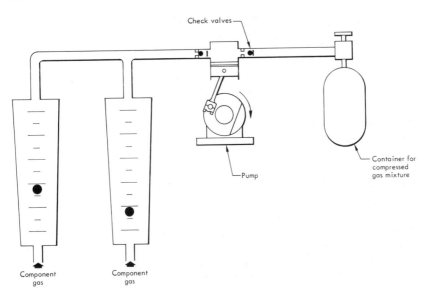

Figure 37. Sketch of a volumetric system for filling test-gas cylinders.

metered and compressed into the storage vessel one at a time. This often leads to a "layering" effect of the gases in the cylinder and incomplete mixing. Methods of mixing are discussed in the section on manometric methods.

The concentration of the individual components is proportional to the ratio of the component volumes to the total volume and can be computed from Equations 41 and 42 in the part-per-million and per cent range respectively.

Volumetric methods enjoy several advantages over most other static calibration methods. Low part-per-million mixtures of non-reactive, nonadsorbing materials can be generated and easily stored for future use with best accuracies at ±2%. Mixtures in the per cent range are also conveniently stored, but explosive mixtures near and above the lower explosive limit must be scrupulously avoided.

Manometric or Partial-Pressure Methods

Test gases can be admitted to steel cylinders in known amounts if the partial pressure of each component is precisely known. Gas cylinders can be pressurized safely to at least 2000 lb/in.^{2} on a routine basis by commercial concerns, but it is not usually advisable or practical for most laboratories to work at these elevated pressures. Nevertheless, gas mixtures can be made using pressures up to 10-12 atmospheres with little specialized equipment.[166,167] Manometric techniques have the advantage that fairly large volumes of complex gas mixtures can be generated and stored for future use. Several cylinders can be filled at the same time for relatively little cost.

A representative manometric system is shown in Figure 38. The cylinders to be filled are connected to a manifold with an appropriate system of gauges over the pressure range of interest. The system should include a gauge in the vacuum region since the manifold is usually evacuated to less than 100 μ before each component gas is admitted to the test-gas cylinder. In the psia range, if large (16-in.) Bourdon-tube gauges are used, an accuracy of 1 part in 500 is claimed and usually proven to be even better.[168] The supply gases are normally connected to a separate manifold, and the two manifolds are connected with a valve.

A typical system is filled using the following procedure. The system of manifolds and cylinders to be filled is evacuated and component 1 flows into the empty cylinders. The desired pressure is reached and recorded, but this must be done slowly to avoid errors from excessive temperature changes.[168] All valves are shut off and the manifold is again evacuated. Component 2 is admitted to the manifold at a pressure slightly in *excess* of component 1 to prevent backflow of the filled component. Component 2 is then admitted to the test cylinder to the desired pressure. Additional components are admitted by repeating this same technique until all have been added. Low part-per-million concentrations can be prepared by evacuating the system and introducing the trace contaminant through the system. This trace material is then swept into a storage cylinder and pressurized with the appropriate dilution gas.[169]

Materials which are normally liquids at room temperature can also be used to fill the cylinder since they exert a certain vapor

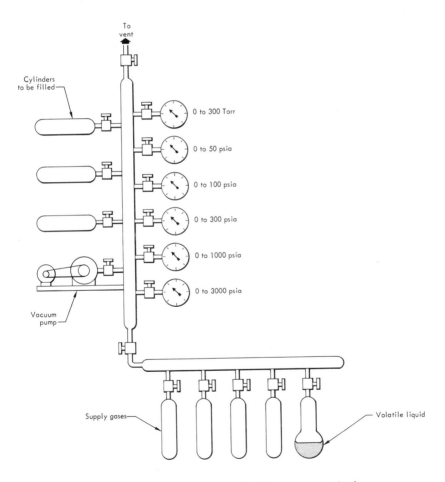

Figure 38. Sketch of a manometric system for filling test-gas cylinders.

pressure, depending on the nature and volatility of the solvent. The vapor pressure of these liquids, however, must be greater than their partial pressure in the gas mixture at the lowest working temperature at which the sample is used. In other words, if the pressure of the system becomes too high (or the temperature too low), the vapors will condense out, and the usable gas mixture will have a variable concentration.

The time required for mixing must also be considered and will depend on vessel size and geometry, injection turbulence, and the interdiffusion coefficients of the gases.[170] The usual mixing procedure is to let the normal diffusion processes intermingle the test gases until homogeneity is obtained. However, this procedure is slow and, in large cylinders, takes days to several weeks to complete. Heating the lower end of the cylinder to 60° C while cooling the upper end to 15° C and inclining the cylinder at a 45° angle still requires about 16 hours to mix the contents.[171] Putting the cylinders on their sides usually cuts the mixing time to about 2 hours, and if the cylinder is rolled, only 8 minutes are required to achieve mixing in large high-pressure (1800-lb/in.²) cylinders of 50% O_2 and 50% N_2.[172] Smaller cylinder and pressure vessels require only a few minutes.[173] Steel shot and marbles have been added to the cylinders to aid in the mixing process.[124]

Computation of the gas-mixture concentration appears to be straightforward if Dalton's law is assumed:

$$P = p_a + p_b + \cdots + p_n , \qquad (51)$$

where P is the total pressure and $p_{a,b \ldots,n}$ are the contributing partial pressures of the component gases. The concentration in per cent by volume of each component at one temperature is

$$C = \frac{10^2 \times p_n}{P} , \qquad (52)$$

and ppm by volume would be

$$C = \frac{10^6 \times p_n}{P} . \qquad (53)$$

At room temperature and pressure, most gases conform to the perfect gas law. However, at elevated pressures the deviation is pronounced, and deviations of ±10 to 20% are not uncommon (as shown in Figure 1). This can sometimes be corrected by defining a new quantity, κ, the compressibility, which is given by

$$\kappa = \frac{PV}{RT} , \qquad (54)$$

where P, V, and T are measured experimentally to yield κ, a correction factor for nonideality. Thus corrected, the concentration of the nth component can be expressed by

$$C_n = \frac{10^2 \times \dfrac{P_n}{\kappa_n}}{\dfrac{P_a}{\kappa'_a} + \dfrac{P_b}{\kappa'_b} + \cdots + \dfrac{P_n}{\kappa'_n}} , \qquad (55)$$

where κ_n is the compressibility of the pure components at the filling pressure and $\kappa'_{a,b,\ldots,n}$ are the compressibilities of the gas mixtures at the final pressure. It must be remembered that as each component is added to the system under pressure, any temperature rise must be accounted for. Either an appropriate calculation correction must be made or the system must be allowed to return to the initial ambient temperature before a pressure reading is made and the next component is added. In general, it is best to add the most compressible gas first unless it happens to be the major component of the mixture. The reason for this is that if the compressible gas is admitted last, it is in the most compressed state and usually introduces the greatest error.[168]

Compressibilities for the pure gases can be found in most chemical engineering handbooks. However, data for gas mixtures are not generally available for all possible combination of gases, temperatures, and pressures, so the value used is usually the one for the pure component.

EXAMPLE 18. Calculate the percentage concentration of a nitrogen, oxygen, and helium mixture when an evacuated vessel is first filled to 200 mm with N_2, to 740 mm with O_2, and then to 5 atm with He. Assume no compressibility correction.

P_{N_2} = 200 mm.

P_{O_2} = 740 mm - 200 mm = 540 mm.

P_{He} = (5 atm $\times$ 760 mm/atm) - 740 mm = 3060 mm.

$$P = 5 \text{ atm} \times 760 \text{ mm/atm} = 3800 \text{ mm}.$$

$$C_{N_2} = \frac{10^2 \times 200 \text{ mm}}{3800 \text{ mm}} = 5.26\%.$$

$$C_{O_2} = \frac{10^2 \times 540 \text{ mm}}{3800 \text{ mm}} = 14.2\%.$$

$$C_{He} = \frac{10^2 \times 3060 \text{ mm}}{3800 \text{ mm}} = 80.5\%.$$

EXAMPLE 19. Calculate the concentrations of a butane, propane, and nitrogen mixture when the tank to be filled is evacuated and filled with butane to 10 lb/in.² ($\kappa = 0.97$ at 10 lb/in.², 0.88 at 3 atm) and propane is then added until a pressure of 3 atm is reached ($\kappa = 0.95$ at 3 atm). Assume that all pressures are recorded at the same ambient temperature.

At 10 lb/in.²,

$$p_{C_4H_{10}} = \frac{10 \text{ lb/in.}^2}{14.7 \text{ lb/in.}^2/\text{atm} \times 0.97} = 0.701 \text{ atm}.$$

At 3 atm,

$$p_{C_4H_{10}} = \frac{10 \text{ lb/in.}^2}{14.7 \text{ lb/in.}^2/\text{atm} \times 0.88} = 0.773 \text{ atm}.$$

At 3 atm,

$$p_{C_3H_8} = \frac{3 \text{ atm}}{0.95} - \left(10 \text{ lb/in.}^2 / 14.7 \text{ lb/in.}^2/\text{atm} \times 0.88\right)$$

$$= 2.38 \text{ atm}.$$

$$C_{C_4H_{10}} = \frac{10^2 \times 0.701 \text{ atm}}{0.773 \text{ atm} + 2.38 \text{ atm}} = 22.2\%.$$

$$C_{C_3H_8} = \frac{10^2 \times 2.38 \text{ atm}}{0.773 \text{ atm} + 2.38 \text{ atm}} = 75.5\%.$$

The 2.3% is unaccounted for because of compressibility errors.

Manometric techniques are used mostly in the laboratory to produce preliminary analytical standards. The routine accuracies attained are usually ±5% at reduced pressures where compressibilities approach unity.[121] These methods can be used to produce mixtures in the per cent range, but gas concentrations as low as 10 ppm have been achieved only after making a pre-blend.[167] Accuracies of ±1% are claimed for blends in the 180–380-ppm range for small containers,[174] and such techniques have been used successfully in producing standards for mass spectrometric analysis.[168,174]

There are several limitations which must be understood before these systems can be employed. Large deviations from the predicted concentrations can occur upon liquefaction of one or more of the components or if compressibility data for the condition of interest are not available for the gaseous mixtures. Deviation from expected values can also occur if the heat created by the compression is not accounted for in the calculation or is not allowed to dissipate before the addition of successive components. Errors also occur from the usual effects of polymerization of certain mixtures (0.5% HCN for example) and decomposition [$Ni(CO)_4$] unless the proper stabilizing agents are added.[100]

Probably the greatest disadvantage of manometric techniques is the inherent danger of working with a pressurized system which may contain reactive mixtures. Pressurizing with pure oxygen when hydrocarbons are present can be hazardous, and certain pure gases such as acetylene and monovinyl acetylene detonate on pressurizing. Other materials which react even though one component is present in ppm quantities include oxygen and hydrogen, chlorine and hydrogen, nitrogen dioxide and nitric acid, and unsaturated hydrocarbons with sulfur-bearing compounds.[121]

Gravimetric Methods

Gravimetric methods are considered to be the most accurate and reproducible techniques of producing primary analytical standards and checking gas-flow measurements.[66] The cylinder or vessel to be filled is weighed before and after the addition of each of the components on a suitable high-load balance. Most commercial manufacturers use specially designed and engineered high-load balances for this purpose. Cylinders such as the lecture bottle and the 7-kg cylinder shown in Table XV can be weighed on commercially available balances. Smaller, specially made containers have also been designed for small volume mixtures.[175] High-

Table XV. Approximate weights and dimensions of commercial cylinders.

Manufacturers' number	Height (in.)	Diameter (in.)	Empty weight (kg)
Lecture bottle, 5	15	2	1.6
4, 12	14 to 22	4	7
3, 30	21 to 27	4 to 6	13
2, 80	19 to 27	7 to 8	30
1, 200	52 to 56	9	60

capacity top-loading balances, for example, can weigh containers from 5 to 11 kg to within ±50 mg. Although the tared weights of cylinders can be recorded to within ±0.0005 g for gas mixtures in the per cent range, a lack of knowledge concerning sample purity, adsorption, and side reactions make this method accurate to between ±0.1 to 0.001%, depending on the magnitude of the concentrations encountered.

Although gravimetric calculations would seem to be trivial, best results are obtained by correcting for any bouyancy changes between measurements. Anything which would affect the air density around the cylinders and balance weights, such as temperature changes, relative humidity, and barometric pressure, must be allowed for. A detailed account of these calculations is given by Miller *et al.*[176] Sample corrections for gas purity in a mixture containing, hydrogen, methane, nitrogen, and helium are shown in Table XVI. Notice that the total weight of any component is the amount added as the pure component plus any which might be present as an impurity in the other components.

The accuracy of a good system should not fall below ±0.1% if the component purity is known and if negligible gas interaction or absorption is present. Values of ±0.05%[66,176] are common, and ±0.002% has been routinely achieved[121] with components in the per cent range. Standards in the ppm range, however, cannot approach this accuracy unless a predilution has been made. Most of the errors inherent in pressurized measurements, such as temperature equilibrium and deviation from ideality, can be neglect-

Table XVI.   Corrections for the purity of component gases.[a]

Components	Mass-spectrometer analysis (mole %)	(wt %)	Weight (g)	Weight corrected for purity (g)	Actual weight (g)
Hydrogen	99.8	97.29	0.3349	0.3258	0.3258
Nitrogen	0.2	2.71	—	0.0091	—
Methane	98.93	97.93	—	11.9763	—
Nitrogen	0.71	1.22	—	0.1492	—
Carbon dioxide	0.21	0.57	12.2294	0.0697	11.9763
Ethane	0.15	0.28	—	0.0342	—
Nitrogen	100.00	100.00	176.4653	176.4653	176.6236[b]
Helium	100.00	100.00	33.1762	33.1762	33.1762
Ethane[c]	—	—	—	—	0.0342
Carbon dioxide[c]	—	—	—	—	0.0697
Total	—	—	222.2058	222.2058	222.2058

[a]Data taken from Reference 176.

[b]The actual weight of N_2 in the mixture is 176.4653 g plus 0.0091 g from the H_2 plus 0.1492 g from the CH_4.

[c]These components were initially present in the methane.

ed. The main disadvantage of the gravimetric system is the expense of the pressurizing equipment and the rather expensive high-load, high-precision balance.

PARTIALLY EVACUATED SYSTEMS

Gaseous mixtures are rarely useful if they are made in a closed container at a pressure of less than 1 atm. Mixtures must usually be transported to another location where the test, standardization, or evaluation takes place. There are, however, several occasions when it is desirable to produce a standard gas mixture at atmospheric pressure or below in a closed vessel for calibration work. A classic example is the production of analytical standards for gas-phase infrared, visible, and ultraviolet absorption measurements.[120,177] This is illustrated in Figure 39.

The major components of the system are an air purifier, an optical cell, a vacuum pump, and a manometric pressure-measuring system. To operate the system, stopcock A is closed and stopcock B is set in the position shown. The system is evacuated to less than 1 mm Hg. Stopcock B is then turned 180 degrees to eliminate the vacuum pump from the system. An appropriate amount of gas or liquid is injected into the cell through a rubber septum as the diluent gas is slowly bled into the cell by just cracking stopcock A. The reduced pressure and flowing gas is normally sufficient to vaporize and mix the component gases. The diluent gases (usually air or nitrogen) must be free from water vapor to prevent fogging of the sodium chloride windows. Carbon dioxide should be removed with Ascarite, for it contains a number of bands which could interfere significantly with the absorption measurements.

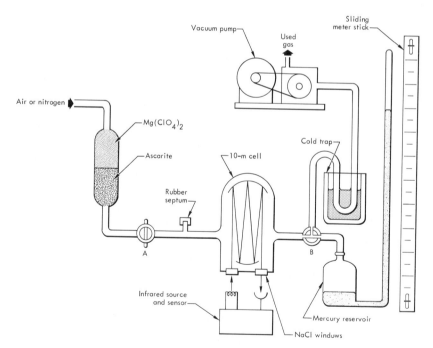

Figure 39. Sketch of a partially evacuated system for producing analytical standards for gas-phase infrared-absorption measurements.

Concentrations are adjusted by pumping the cell down to a known pressure and diluting with more gas. Usually, the most concentrated standard is measured first, and progessively more dilute standards are made by adjusting the pressure ratios.

The accuracy of the system just described is ±1 to 5% and depends on the concentration desired and the magnitude of the pressure dilution made. If a 10–100-fold dilution is made, the error involved will be larger than if a two- or three-fold dilution is made. Materials which are readily adsorbed, reacted, or polymerized should be scrupulously avoided, for they can adversely affect the optics of a multiple-pass absorption cell.

DeGrazia and Auge[178] have developed a somewhat similar method for producing mixtures of C_1 to C_4 hydrocarbons in helium. The system is similarly evacuated and trace gases are introduced until the required pressure is attained and noted with a 0–1000-mm-Hg precision pressure dial. In this manner, a somewhat better accuracy of ±4% is obtained in the per cent range, but a decrease to ±15% in the 100-ppm range is noted.

The starting concentration of the mixtures of interest can be computed from Equations 41 and 42 for gases and from Equations 43, 44, and 46 for liquids.

When injecting liquids or gases into a nearly evacuated system, the dead volume of the syringe needle must be taken into account, especially when generating parts-per-million concentrations in small-volume systems. Syringe dead volume is not always constant and depends a great deal on the solvent employed, the syringe type, and the needle configuration as well as on the prevailing experimental conditions. King and Dupre, for example, show the dead volume for methanol (0.30 μl) to be more than twice that of water (0.13 μl) when using certain 5-μl syringes.[179] Experimentally, dead volumes for each syringe can be determined by making absorption measurements at various apparent syringe volumes, plotting them, and extrapolating them to zero absorbance. Figure 40 shows the results of three sets of such measurements carried out on a typical 10-μl syringe with a 2-in. needle. Notice that the dead volumes are 0.45, 0.60, and 0.80 μl, an appreciably large error even when the syringe is used at full capacity.

Concentration changes are made by evacuating the system. The resulting concentration is then computed from

$$C = c_0 \frac{P}{P_0} , \qquad (56)$$

where c_o is the initial concentration in either parts per million or per cent, P is the new reduced pressure, and p_o is the starting pressure.

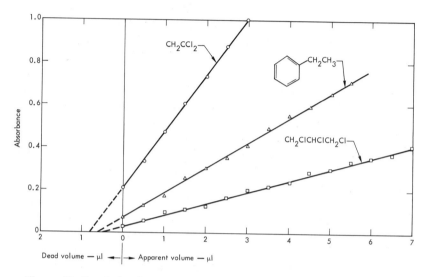

Figure 40. Graph for determining the dead volume of a syringe. The actual syringe volume injected is the sum of the apparent and the dead volumes.

EXAMPLE 20. What volume of methane in air is needed to produce a concentration of 750 ppm in an 8.05-liter cell at a test pressure of 1 atm? What pressure reduction is required to achieve a final concentration of 450 ppm?

From Equation 41,

$$v_C = 10^{-6} \times Cv_D = 750 \text{ ppm} \times 8.05 \text{ liters} \times 10^{-6} = 6.04 \times 10^{-3} \text{ liters} = 6.04 \text{ ml.}$$

$$P = \frac{Cp_0}{c_0} = \frac{450 \text{ ppm} \times 760 \text{ mm}}{750 \text{ ppm}} = 456 \text{ mm.}$$

EXAMPLE 21. What is the apparent volume of benzene required to produce a concentration of 200 ppm in a 7.35-liter absorption cell at 700 mm Hg and 25°C? The needle dead volume is 1.2 μl.

From Equation 46,

$$v_L = \frac{200 \text{ ppm} \times 78.1 \text{ g/mole} \times 7.35 \text{ liters} \times 273°C \times 700 \text{ mm Hg}}{(22.4 \times 10^6 \text{ liters/mole}) \times 0.880 \text{ g/ml} \times 298°C \times 760 \text{ mm Hg}} = 0.00491 \text{ ml.}$$

The apparent syringe volume is then

$$4.91 \ \mu l - 1.2 \ \mu l = 3.7 \ \mu l.$$

Chapter 5

Dynamic Systems for Producing Gas Mixtures

The dynamic method of generating gas and vapor mixtures requires the continuous and uninterrupted blending of the component parts for some specified period of time. This technique enjoys many advantages over static methods and is especially useful in producing reactive gas mixtures. If the mixture is prone to decomposition or chemical reaction, the undesirable reaction products can be swept away and continuously replaced by the relatively pure and unreacted test-gas mixture. Large volumes of the test mixture can be produced for extended time intervals, and concentrations from 50% down to the part-per-billion range can be controlled and altered easily with conveniently compact equipment. Wall adsorption, a problem in most static systems, usually becomes negligible since an equilibrium is established after operating for a long enough time period. These general advantages are, however, sometimes offset by the cost and complexity of many dynamic methods, especially those required for producing ppm and ppb mixtures from pure starting materials.

Dynamic methods have a much wider range of applicability than the static or closed systems. In any operation where unwanted waste gases must be swept away, they are indispensible. For example, in toxicological, inhalation, and odor investigations where oxygen and the gas of interest are consumed and carbon dioxide and water vapor are produced, a test mixture can be continuously supplied to maintain the desired component concen-

95

tration. Other areas of applicability include gas-phase catalytic and kinetic studies, adsorption and absorption measurements, gas-irradiation experiments and analytical standards. Dynamic methods are especially useful for continuously producing standards for gas-phase infrared spectrophotometry and direct-reading gas measuring instrumentation.

The dynamic systems discussed in this chapter include gas-stream mixing, injection, diffusion, permeation, evaporation, electrolysis, and continuous chemical reactions.

GAS-STREAM MIXING

Single Dilution

The most widely used and successful method of mixing two or more gases is to dilute the gases with one another after measuring their flow rates.[18,140] Figure 41 shows the components of a test mixture being initially metered through previously calibrated rotameters (see Chapter 3). They are subsequently recombined into a single test mixture after passing through a mixing chamber. If the flowmeters are operating smoothly and the indicator ball is not oscillating excessively, no mixing chamber is necessary. The turbulence of the entering components is normally sufficient to promote homogeneous mixing at the end of a normal length of tubing before exiting.[180]

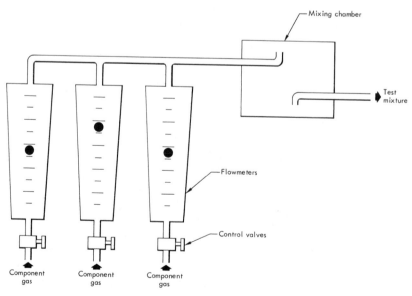

Figure 41. Sketch of a typical system for mixing three-component gas streams.

Gases can either be metered or pumped as pure component,[181-192] or be previously diluted[77,193-199] to facilitate high dilution. Dilutions of 1000:1 can be routinely achieved with commercial flowmeters, and dilutions of 10,000:1 can be accomplished if a high-volume flowmeter is chosen. The extreme low end of the flowmeter range should not be used as accuracy will be sacrificed. Generalized flow-rate ranges are shown in Table XVII. Any of those shown may be used with any other in any given system. If small-volume dispensers (*i.e.*, porous plugs) are to be diluted with relatively high diluent-gas flows, care must be taken to keep the inlets as small and short as possible. With too large an inlet, excessively long time periods are required to reach equilibrium.[77] Figure 42 shows an example of such an inlet. The 0.5-mm-i.d. nozzle passes flows up to 0.3 liter/min with only a fraction of an inch pressure drop.[77]

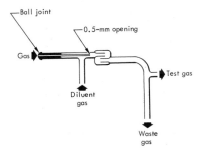

Figure 42. Sketch of a system with a low-flow inlet for making single dilutions.

In addition to those flowmeters shown in Table XVII, mixing pumps which combine gases pumped through pistons at adjustable speeds and rotating stopcocks which add the trace-gas pulses to a diluent-gas stream are also available.[157] The methods chosen, however, are normally rotameters or orifice meters.[181] Direct reading "Dyna-blenders" are available commercially[92] which directly read out the contaminant and total flow rate for easy calculation.

Equipment for any dynamic system is usually made with as inert a material as possible and practical. Glass and Teflon are normally used, and long sections of rubber and polymeric tubing should be avoided, especially when corrosive and reactive mixtures are involved. For example, a 1-in. section of Tygon tubing has been known to reduce a 0.1-ml/min flow of chlorine gas by one-half.[77]

Table XVII.   Ranges of various flow rate measuring devices.

Type	Range
Rotameter	1 ml/min to 300 ft^3/min
Wet test meter	1 to 80 liters/min
Dry gas meter	5 to 5000 liters/min
Critical orifice	>10 ml/min
Orifice meter	5 ml/min to 50 liters/min
Controlled leak	>10^{-8} ml/sec
Asbestos-plug flowmeter	0.01 to 100 ml/min
Heated-wire anemometer	0.1 ml/min to 300 ft^3/min
Heated thermistor	1 ml/min to 1000 ft^3/min
Heated thermocouple	0.01 ml/min to 200 ft^3/min
Pitot tube	>600 ft/min
Drag-body flowmeter	>1 liter/min
Rotating-vane anemometer	50 to 24,000 ft/min

The concentration calculation for a single-dilution dynamic system is

$$c_a = \frac{10^2 \times q_a}{q_a + q_b + \cdots + q_n} , \qquad (57)$$

where

c_a = concentration of component a (per cent) and

$q_{a,b,\ldots,n}$ = flow rate of the individual pure components (volume/unit time).

If component a is not pure, then Equation 57 becomes

$$c_a = \frac{10^2 \times Xq_a}{q_a + q_b + \cdots + q_n} , \qquad (58)$$

where X is the mole fraction or decimal per cent of purity by volume.

The concentration in parts per million can be calculated from

$$c_a = \frac{10^6 \times q_a}{q_D} , \tag{59}$$

where q_D is the diluent-gas flow rate. Again, if the component gas is not pure, Equation 57 becomes

$$c_a = \frac{10^6 \times Xq_a}{q_D} . \tag{60}$$

EXAMPLE 22. What flow rate of carbon monoxide is required to produce a 20% concentration in a stream of nitrogen flowing at 10 ft^3/min?

$$C_{CO} = \frac{q_{CO}}{q_{CO} + q_{N_2}} .$$

$$q_{CO} = \frac{C_{CO}\, q_{N_2}}{1 - C_{CO}} = \frac{0.20 \times 10 \text{ ft}^3/\text{min} \times 28.3 \text{ liters}/\text{ft}^3}{1 - 0.20}$$

$$= 70.8 \text{ liters}/\text{min.}$$

EXAMPLE 23. What flow rate of air is required to produce a concentration of 1.5 ppm chlorine when mixed with a 1% chlorine and air mixture flowing at 3 ml/min?

$$q_{air} = \frac{10^6 \times q_{Cl_2}\, X_{Cl_2}}{C_{Cl_2}} = \frac{10^6 \times 3 \text{ ml}/\text{min} \times 0.01}{1.5 \text{ ppm}}$$

$$= 20 \text{ liters}/\text{min.}$$

Often, it is desirable to know how long it takes any given test-gas stream to fill a test chamber of known dimensions. Assuming perfect and instantaneous mixing, such a computation can be carried out using a modification of Equation 47 as follows[138]:

$$C = c_0\left(1 - e^{-Q\tau/V}\right), \tag{61}$$

where

C = resultant concentration (% or ppm),
c_0 = initial concentration (% or ppm),
Q = total flow rate through the chamber (liters/min),
τ = time required to achieve concentration C (min), and
V = total chamber volume (liters).

Rearranging and taking logs,

$$2.303 \log \frac{c_0}{c_0 - C} = \frac{Q\tau}{V} . \tag{62}$$

$$\tau = 2.303 \frac{V}{Q} \log \frac{c_0}{c_0 - C} . \tag{63}$$

EXAMPLE 24. How long would it take to fill a 20-m³ chamber to a concentration of 5 ppm using a 20-ppm contaminant gas flowing at 50 liters/min?

$$\tau = 2.303 \frac{20 \times 10^3 \text{ liters}}{50 \text{ liters/min}} \log \frac{20}{20 - 5} .$$

$$\tau = 115 \text{ min.}$$

EXAMPLE 25. What is the time required to purge any size chamber until it is 99.9% filled with the test gas? Express the answer in terms of V and Q.

$$\tau_{99.9} = 2.303 \frac{V}{Q} \log \frac{100}{100 - 99.9} = 2.303 \frac{V}{Q} \log 10^3 .$$

$$\tau_{99.9} = 6.91 \frac{V}{Q} .$$

The accuracy of single-stage dilution has been reported by Roccanova to be ±1 to 3% of the component value in the per cent and ppm range and ±3 to 5% in the ppb range.[121] These percentages will largely depend on knowledge of the initial starting-material purity.

Double Dilution

It is often desirable to generate a low ppm concentration while avoiding high dilution ratios and the use of extremely low-flow rotameters. This can be accomplished by using a double-dilution technique as shown in Figure 43.[77,200-203] The contaminant and diluent gases are combined after adjusting the flow-rate-control valves of rotameters A and B just as in the single-stage dilution system. A portion of the mixture is then exited to the atmosphere and the flow rate of the remainder through rotameter C is controlled by adjusting the bleed-off valves. More diluent gas enters through rotameter D, and the mixture is further diluted. Using this method, the initial contaminant gas can be diluted by four to nine orders of magnitude.

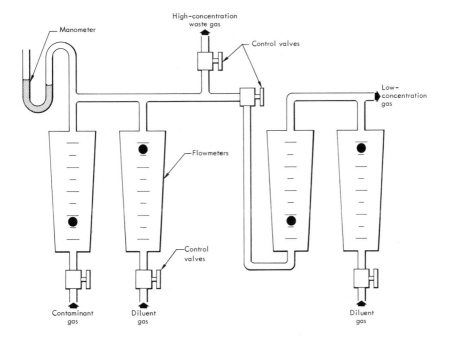

Figure 43. Sketch of a system for making double dilutions.

Calculations for double or any multiple dilution are based on Equation 58 and can be expressed for an n-stage dilution by

$$C = 10^2 \times X \left[\frac{q_{a_1}}{q_{a_1} + q_{D_1}} \right] \left[\frac{q_{a_2}}{q_{a_2} + q_{D_2}} \right] \cdots \left[\frac{q_{a_n}}{q_{a_n} + q_{D_n}} \right] \quad (64)$$

where

C = resultant concentration (per cent),

$q_{a_{1,2,...,n}}$ = flow rate of contaminant a at stage 1, 2, ..., n (liters/min),

$q_{D_{1,2,...,n}}$ = flow rate of diluent gas at stage 1, 2, ..., n (liters/min), and

X = contaminant purity (mole fraction).

It must be remembered that as each stage is added, pressure buildups in each previous stage must be determined and corrected, using Equations 42 and 43.

EXAMPLE 26. Hydrochloric acid (97% pure by volume) flows at 20 ml/min and is diluted by dry air flowing at a rate 1.0 ft³/min. One per cent of the resultant concentration is again diluted with 30 liters/min of air. The pressure differential between the ambient air and the first stage is 6 in. H_2O, while a negligible pressure is observed between the second stage and the ambient air. If the ambient pressure is 745 mm Hg, calculate the concentration of HCL in parts per million.

The concentration of HCl exiting from the first stage is

$$C_1 = (0.97) \frac{(20 \text{ ml/min}) 10^6}{(1.0 \text{ ft}^3/\text{min})(28.3 \times 10^3 \text{ ml/ft}^3)}$$

$$= 686 \text{ ppm}$$

If 1% of the C_1 flow rate (0.283 liters/min) is further diluted at a different pressure, then the resultant concentration from the second stage is

$$C_2 = 686 \text{ ppm} \times \left[\frac{745 \text{ mm} + (6 \text{ in.}/0.535 \text{ in.}/\text{mm})}{745 \text{ mm}} \right]$$

$$\times \left[\frac{0.283 \text{ liters/min}}{0.283 \text{ liters/min} + 30 \text{ liters/min}} \right].$$

$$C_2 = 6.5 \text{ ppm}.$$

Purge-time calculations are made with Equation 63 just as for a single-stage dilution.

Although the multiple-dilution technique would seem to be simple enough, it actually becomes somewhat difficult after more than two dilutions. Rotameters have been observed to oscillate widely,[204] and a variety of resonances and instabilities make them extremely hard to control.[145] Moreover, as each stage is added, pressure buildups are inevitable and corrections become increasingly more difficult. Accuracies better than ±5 to 10% are common after a typical two-stage dilution, although 2% has been reported by Schnelle.[201] Another disadvantage of the serial-dilution method is the tremendous amount of contaminant gas which is wasted after each dilution stage. Fully 99% of the test gas is normally bled off and not used in making up the test atmosphere.

INJECTION METHODS

Gases and liquids can be added to moving gas streams by a wide variety of mechanical dosers, injectors, and pumps as well as gravity and electrolytic feeding units. The early attempts at producing standard test atmospheres containing one or more components used motor-driven syringes, belt drives, and geared mechanisms, and these methods, using modern speed-control units, can generate gas mixtures of high accuracy and precision over extended time intervals. The concentrations generated can extend from the per cent range to fractions of a part per million. Such methods are particularly useful in preparing analytical standards for instruments which continuously monitor a particular gas or vapor concentration and are used for gas detector instrument calibration and for gas-phase infrared and gas chromatography standards. Such methods find themselves worthwhile in adsorption and absorption measurements and also in studying relatively slow chemical reactions by feeding in reactants at known, controlled rates.

An idealized feed system is shown in Figure 44. The diluent-gas supply is pressure-regulated and an appropriate flow rate chosen. Gas or liquid is forced into the injection port by some dispensing device such as a pump, a motor-driven syringe, a piston, or an electrolytic or gravity feed mechanism. If a liquid is involved, some method must be employed to vaporize and dispense it evenly into the moving diluent-gas stream. A cooling unit is sometimes needed to remove or exchange unwanted heat if a heater is used to assist in the vaporization operation. A mixing chamber is required if the contaminant gases or vapors are added unevenly or if surges exist in the diluent-gas flow or the vaporization process. A control unit is provided to alter feeding rates and to provide thermostatic control, if desired, over the evaporator.

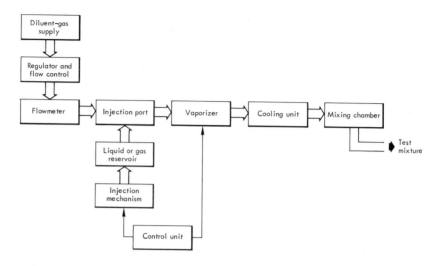

Figure 44. Block diagram of the major components in a dynamic injection system.

Motor-Driven Injectors

Liquid Reservoirs

Motor-driven feeding devices have been used extensively to introduce gases, liquids, vapors, and even particulate matter into moving gas streams. The material to be injected is contained in some type of inert reservoir, the volume of which diminishes evenly when acted upon by the mechanical dispensing apparatus. Syringes have been long employed for this purpose,[205,206] and several types currently used and available are discussed in Chapter 4. Gas-tight syringes with a Teflon-tipped barrel are particularly useful for injecting most liquids or gases, but syringes made entirely of Teflon must be used in special instances such as when working with hydrogen fluoride. When making slow-speed injections, syringes made entirely of glass usually lose some material, particularly if it is a liquid, between the glass interfaces, and they are subject to large delivery errors, especially in the microliter-per-minute injection range. Syringes are available with 0.05–50-ml capacities and will deliver from 0.5–500 μl/min when dispensed at moderate or slow speeds.

Syringes can be used to make injections one at a time (Figure 45A),[207-214] two or more at a time (Figure 45B),[188,206,215-219] or alternately where one injects while the other fills itself from the reservoir (Figure 45C).[141] During long running times, some air may accumulate in the syringe, but this can be kept as low as 0.1 ml/day if tubing connections are short and system integrity is maintained.[141]

Syringe delivery rates will, of course, vary with syringe capacity

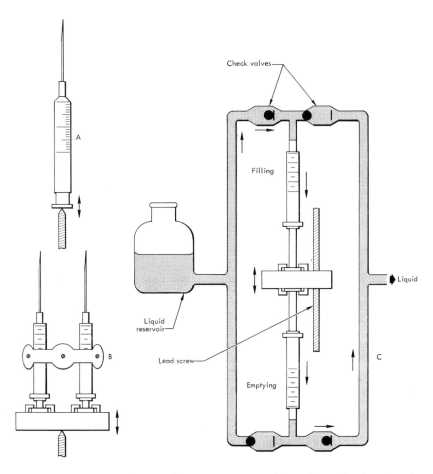

Figure 45. Sketch of a single-syringe injector (A) and two kinds of multiple-syringe injectors (B and C). The check valves in C permit the syringes to alternately fill and empty as the lead screw moves up and down.

and the rate of plunger advance. The amount of liquid dispensed for various syringe capacities and lead-screw advance rates is shown in Table XVIII. Commercial syringe dispensers will deliver from as low as 0.79 μl/min to as high as 720 ml/min if 2- and 50-ml syringes are used.[220]

The syringe should be mounted in an upright position if the best contact is to be made with the lead screw. This is not,

Table XVIII. Guide for determining the volume dispensed from variously sized syringes.

Thread size (threads/in.)	0.05 ml and 60 mm	0.1 ml and 60 mm	0.25 ml and 60 mm	0.50 ml and 60 mm	1.0 ml and 60 mm	2.5 ml and 60 mm	5.0 ml and 60 mm	10 ml and 61.8 mm	20 ml and 66.4 mm	30 ml and 72 mm	50 ml and 80.8 mm	100 ml and 102.5 mm
13	1.63	3.25	8.14	16.3	32.5	81.4	163	314	588	790	1208	1534
16	1.32	2.64	6.62	13.2	26.4	66.2	132	256	478	642	982	1246
18	1.18	2.35	5.88	11.8	23.5	58.8	118	227	425	571	873	1108
20	1.06	2.11	5.29	10.6	21.1	52.9	106	204	382	514	785	997
24	0.882	1.76	4.40	8.82	17.6	44.0	88.2	170	318	428	654	830
28	0.756	1.51	3.78	7.56	15.1	37.8	75.6	146	273	367	561	712
32	0.662	1.32	3.31	6.62	13.2	33.1	66.2	128	239	321	491	623
40	0.529	1.06	2.65	5.29	10.6	26.5	52.9	102	191	257	393	498
48	0.441	0.880	2.20	4.41	8.80	22.0	44.1	85.2	159	214	327	415

Dispensed volume (in µl) with one rotation of the lead screw for syringes with volumes and lengths of:

however, absolutely necessary if the plunger is snugly fit and clamped in some fashion to the driving arm. Syringe mantles or removable glass jackets can be added to maintain constant temperatures or to circulate heating or cooling media to ensure that the material being injected is maintained at the proper phase.

Other reservoirs such as ultramicroburets have been used,[144] but some difficulties have been encountered when filling because of the general fragility of the glassware and the presence of the mercury interface.

Drive Motors

Syringes, microburets, or any other contaminant reservoirs can be emptied smoothly and evenly with a variety of techniques, but some type of electromechanical system utilizing a motor is preferred and is often superior to other methods. Both synchronous single-speed motors alone or with gear reducers and variable-speed DC systems have wide general appeal, and several techniques are summarized briefly in Table XIX and shown in Figure 46.

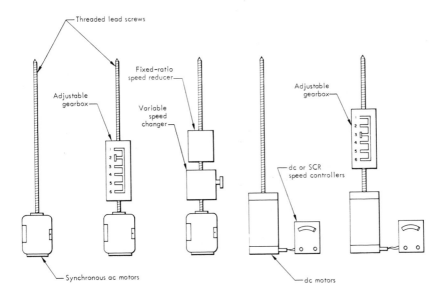

Figure 46. Sketch of several motor speed-control systems showing synchronous, stepped, and continously variable controls.

Table XIX. Characteristics of motor-driven injection systems.

Motor	Speed selector	Speed range	Number of speeds	Reproducibility (%)	Power supply	Reduction gear
ac synchronous	Direct drive	1:1	1	±0.1	None	None
ac synchronous	Mechanical adjustable gear box	$1:10^4$	2 to 30	±0.25	None	None
ac synchronous	Variable-ratio gear box	1:25	Infinite within range	±0.33	None	Required
dc	Electronic	1:10	Infinite within range	±5	Ordinary dc power supply	None
dc	Electronic	1:20 to 1:50	Infinite within range	±3	SCR controller	None
dc	Electronic and mechanical	$1:10^5$	Infinite within range	±3	SCR controller	Required

The most widely used drive motor is the synchronous AC timing motor, and several applications are listed in References 207, 213, and 221. They provide a constant rpm at moderate and light torques since they depend only on line frequency for their speed control. Such motors are small, inexpensive, and easy to wire, maintain, and operate. Variable-speed AC motors such as universal series wound types using some sort of voltage-regulating power-stat are not successful because the rpm's will vary with the load at any given power setting. One of the most successful motors is a single-phase, capacitor, three-lead motor. This provides a constant speed and a low starting torque, and it is reversible during operation. If control of an AC motor is desired, the number of activated poles can be changed (some multiple of two). For example, an eight-pole motor can yield 3600, 1800, 1200, or 900 rpm if eight, six, four, or two poles are used respectively. Full speed control can be achieved by changing the frequency to the motor,[222] but this requires equipment and motors whose cost is excessive, especially when speed control can be solved satisfactorily by other, less expensive techniques.

The most dependable speed control of AC timing motors can be done with direct mechanical gear changers. By substituting gear ratios, dual,[144] triple,[211] and even 30 speed steps are currently commercially available[220] and have been used successfully.[141,217,218] Pulleys should be avoided because of slippage differentials at various loads, and only mechanical linkages of gears or chain drives should be used.

Infinitely variable mechanical speed changers are available which yield a high accuracy and precision, and examples are shown in Figure 47. The drive mechanism consists of two toroid-shaped discs coupled to the shafts and drive rollers which transmit rotation between the two discs. Drive rollers are mounted in adjustable gimbals so that they contact the discs at equal but variable radii from the center of the disc. Thus, the ratio of speeds between the two discs is continuously variable as the gimbals are rotated. The discs are not attached to the shafts but are torsion-coupled to them with ball-bearing crown-type cam sets which press the discs inward against the drive rollers with a force proportional to the torque being transmitted. The sloping surfaces of cams are such that the contact pressure is always more than sufficient to prevent excessive slippage when operated within the torque rating of the unit. There is some slippage at lower input speeds, but if the input is kept over 100 rpm and an output gear reducer used, reproducibilities of $\pm 0.33\%$ are common when a ten-turn microdial is used as a speed control.[223]

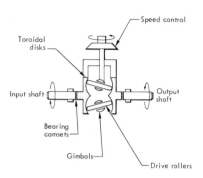

Figure 47. Sketch of a mechanical, continuously variable motor-speed control. (Taken from Reference 223.)

If stepless speed control is required, then variable speed DC motors may be used, but usually some reproducibility must be sacrificed as shown in Table XIX. The DC power supplies available will usually drive a motor over a 10:1 speed range. The newer SCR motor-speed controllers extend this to 50:1. Since the output of a typical DC motor not only varies with load, temperature, humidity, and a host of other factors, the best reproducibility is ±3%, with ±5% being more typical, especially at lower rpm's. These systems, used in conjunction with a variable-ratio gear box, extend the working delivery range over five orders of magnitude, which is enough to make such systems applicable for both the per cent and the parts-per-million ranges at a given air flow. Such systems, however, require a separate power supply but do not normally require a separate reduction-gear system.

All motor-driven systems, whether AC or DC, should have limit or reversing switches to prevent the motor from driving the systems to the extreme end, binding, and eventually burning out or ruining the syringe or injection apparatus. An automatic forward and reversing switch is necessary for continuous running of alternately filling and discharging syringes.

Injection Ports, Mixers, and Evaporators

Gases are relatively easy to inject into a larger flowing volume of gas, but liquids present a somewhat greater problem. They must be injected, evaporated, and mixed smoothly for reliable and invariant gas-mixture concentrations. Injectors for either gases or liquids are most often a narrow-gauge needle. The smaller the flow rate into the diluent gas, the smaller the needle diameter should be to minimize the time to achieve equilibrium. Several injection ports are shown in Figure 48. The most common is a glass tee fitted with a rubber serum cap (Figure 48A) or a rubber septum (Figure 48C).

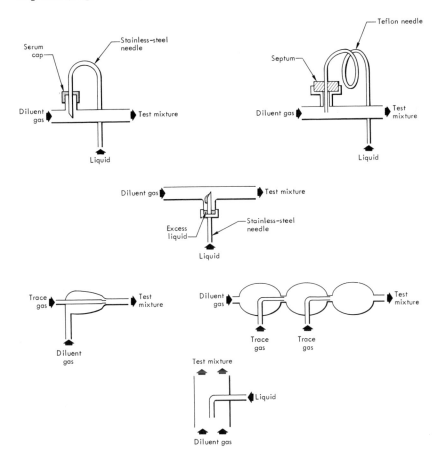

Figure 48. Sketches of several methods for injecting liquids and gases.

The gas or liquid of interest can be injected into the air stream without leakage around the needle point. The injection port shown in Figure 48B is not recommended for liquids because the liquid runs down the needle, is trapped, and is slow to evaporate because of lack of turbulence. Some solvents are lost altogether because of leakage and permeability through the septum.

Needles used for injection should be as inert as possible, and both Teflon and 304 stainless steel are commercially available in a wide variety of lengths and diameters. Table XX gives a summary of some typical needle characteristics. The stainless-steel or hypodermic needles are quite inexpensive but have the disadvantage of being rigid. Steel needles may be bent if special care is taken

Table XX. Specifications of some commercially available hypodermic needles.[a]

Material[b]	Gage	Outside diameter[c] (mm)	Inside diameter[c] (mm)
S	37	0.076	0.025
S	36	0.10	0.05
S	35	0.13	0.05
S	34	0.18	0.076
S	33	0.20	0.10
S	32	0.23	0.10
S	31	0.25	0.13
S, T	30	0.30	0.15
S	29	0.33	0.18
S, T	28	0.36	0.15
S, P	27	0.41	0.20
S, T, P	26	0.47	0.115
S	25	0.51	0.25
S, T	24	0.56	0.30
S	23	0.64	0.33
S, T. P	22	0.71	0.41
S	21	0.81	0.51
S, T	20	0.89	0.58
S, T	19	1.07	0.69
S, T, P	18	1.24	0.84
S, T	17	1.47	1.07
S, T	16	1.65	1.19
S, T	15	1.82	1.37
S, T	14	2.10	1.60
S, T	13	2.41	1.80
S, T	12	2.76	2.16
S, T	11	3.05	2.38
S, T	10	3.40	2.68
T	9	—	—
T	1/8	—	—
T	8	—	—
T	7	—	—

[a] The needles used are those described in Reference 113.

[b] S - stainless steel, T - Teflon, P - platinum.

[c] Stainless-steel needles only.

not to crimp or close off the needle to normal flow. The Teflon needle, on the other hand, is quite flexible, permitting remote placement of the syringe or reservoir, but it is not yet available in very small diameters. Platinum needles in selected gauges (usually 18, 22, 26, and 27) are also available for special uses.

Vaporization Techniques

When liquids must be added to the moving gas stream, some means must be provided to evaporate them smoothly so that the controlled addition of vapors will proceed evenly. If the concentration of a more volatile material at 100 ppm or less is desired, the turbulence of the diluent gas is frequently sufficient to evaporate the material satisfactorily. However, as the concentration requirements increase and the solvent volatility decreases, there comes a time when the normal turbulence is not enough and other methods must be employed to aid the vaporization processes.

There are three main methods of enhancing the evaporation process: (1) the surface area between the diluent gas and the liquid can be increased, (2) the solvent can be heated, and (3) the amount of turbulence around the drops can be increased.

The surface area can easily be increased by adding a plug of glass wool,[208,224] a wick, filter paper,[61] or some type of gauze or cheese cloth.[225,226] If the evaporation tube is oriented vertically, the liquid will migrate down the gauze and gradually be removed by the diluent gas passing upward. Hence, the liquid does not form pools in the bottom of the tube. One must be careful when evaporating small amounts of liquid, for evaporation sometimes does not proceed as smoothly as one might imagine. When the liquid evaporates, it cools the substrate material, retarding the volatilization of the additive liquid. A pulsing concentration gradient then develops.

The vaporization of the liquid can be achieved with a wide variety of heaters. The usual procedure is to heat the diluent gas, which in turn vaporizes the solvent. Several of these are shown in Figure 49. The diluent gas can be passed through a straight or coiled tube and heated with a flame,[227] a combustion furnace, Nichrome wires, heating tape,[217,226,228] steam,[229] or in-line heaters of stainless steel or preferably ceramic.[209,210,230] Figure 50 shows a data curve for a 200-W heater at various air flow rates. Pressure-sensitive tape-on electrical-resistance heaters[231] as well as Electrofilm[398] and spray-on heating elements show great promise.

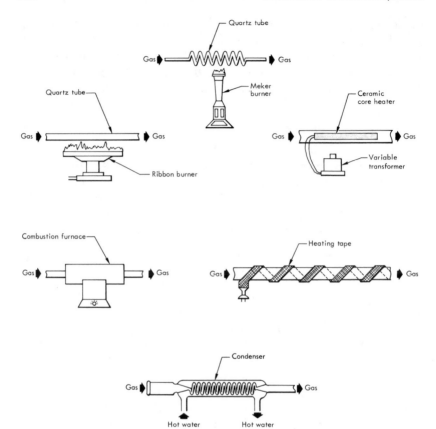

Figure 49. Sketches of several methods for heating gases so that they can later vaporize liquids.

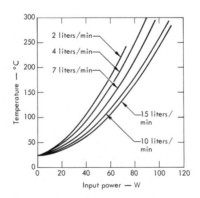

Figure 50. Temperature versus power for a 200-W ceramic heater at various air flow rates.

The last alternative is to increase the turbulence at the point of injection. Either the gas turbulence can cause the required vaporization or the liquid can be atomized into an aerosol, which effectively increases the surface area. Figure 51 shows a basic type of such a device.[18,214,221,232] The liquid is usually fed into the system through a small stainless-steel needle around which the diluent gas stream flows at a high velocity. The force of the gas striking the emerging liquid, as well as the shape of the nozzle, causes the liquid to disperse into small droplets that are in turn quickly vaporized in the moving gas stream. For liquids, the needles should be as small as possible to prevent excessive diffusion when the syringe drive is inactivated.

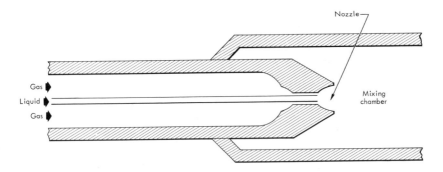

Figure 51. Sketch of a typical atomizer for vaporizing liquids.

A Typical System

The list of alternatives for assembling such dynamic systems is indeed large and will, of course, depend on budget and resource considerations as well as glass-blowing and mechanical-shop capabilities at the interested laboratory.

A system which will produce known concentrations of gas and solvent vapor for calibration work in the 1–2000-ppm range for a single trace contaminant in air has been developed. It is accurate to ±1% if a precision flowmeter is used and has been calibrated at the desired laboratory conditions. The apparatus (see Figure 52) consists of an air cleaner, a solvent-injection system, and a combination mixing and cooling chamber.

Compressed air from a two-stage regulator and needle valve pases into a filtering system, where it is cleaned by Drierite, soda lime, and charcoal. Other methods of air purification as outlined in Chapter 3 may be used, depending on the amount of contamination present in the incoming air supply. The air flow rate is

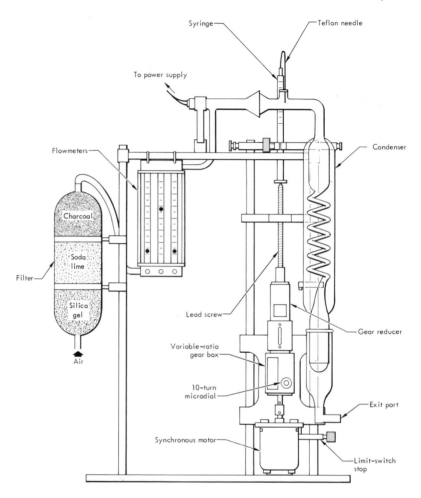

Figure 52. Sketch of a dynamic variable-speed injector system.

measured by a calibrated flowmeter and heated with a ceramic
200-W heater to vaporize the solvent. No air heating is necessary
when gas is injected. The air temperature is measured by a pyrometer; it is uaually about 5°C above the boiling point of the
solvent, but the exact air temperature will depend on the magnitude of the concentration produced and the air flow rate. The heat
applied should leave a small drop about 1 to 2 needle diameters in
width on the tip of the Teflon needle in the injection syringe.
Close inspection should show the drop maintaining a uniform size
throughout a test at a given concentration.

The solvent is introduced into the heated air stream by a

gas-tight, Teflon-tipped syringe fitted with a 5-in., 22-gauge Teflon needle (see Figure 53). The size of the syringe, usually 0.05–50 ml, depends on the magnitude of the concentrations to be produced. The syringe plunger is driven by a 280-rpm synchronous motor controlled by a variable-ratio gear box fitted with a 100:1 fixed gear reducer, as illustrated in Figure 54. Output motor speeds are changed by varying the settings of a 10-turn microdial. As the syringe lead screw (28 threads/in.) rotates in its stationary mounted assembly, the lead screw and the motor platform rise and cause the syringe plunger to depress. Hence, if the motor turns at a constant speed, the solvent or gas is introduced into the air stream at a uniform rate. Table XXI illustrates the condition for a few sample solvents and gases.[209]

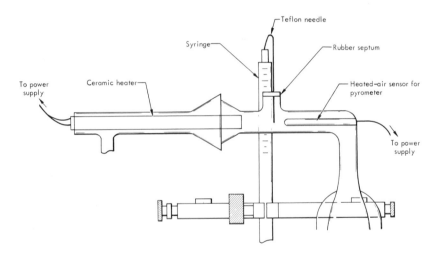

Figure 53. Close-up of the injection port in Figure 52. The contaminant gas or liquid enters through the Teflon needle.

A Graham condenser with ground-glass joints cools the vapor and air mixture to room temperature. Either water or air can be circulated as a cooling agent. After cooling, the vapor and air mixture can be used to obtain a calibration point. The temperature of the gas mixture is monitored with a second pyrometer to ensure that it is at room temperature. This eliminates the necessity of temperature corrections.

A power supply for the syringe-drive motor is a switchbox that activates and rewinds the lead screw. It also contains a Variac that controls the air temperature of the ceramic heater. In addition, both pyrometers that monitor the air temperature are housed in

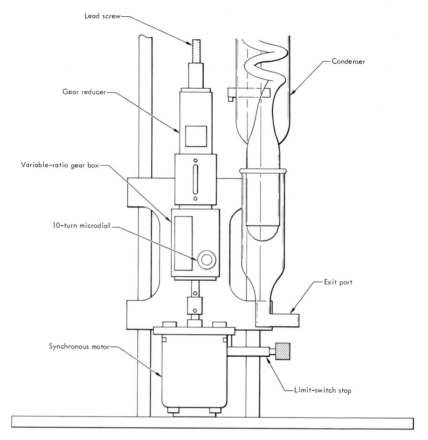

Figure 54. Close-up of the speed-control system in Figure 52.

the power-supply section. Limit switches on the motor platform stop the motor when the syringe plunger is fully opened or depressed.

Calculations

For liquids the concentration in ppm produced from a motor-driven syringe, assuming ideality, is

$$
C = \frac{(22.4 \times 10^{6}) \times \dfrac{T}{273^\circ K} \times \dfrac{760 \text{ mm}}{P} \times n_W q_L \, \rho}{q_D M} \, , \quad (65)
$$

where

C = concentration of the trace material (ppm),
T = experimental temperature (°K),
P = experimental pressure (mm Hg),

Table XXI. Conditions for producing various concentrations of gas and solvent vapors.

Contaminant	Concentration produced (ppm)	Motor speed (rpm)	Syringe capacity (ml)	Syringe delivery rate (µl/revolution)	Air flow (liters/min)
Acetone	100	0.500	0.500	7.56	12.6
	2000	10.0			
Carbon monoxide	25	0.500	20.0	273.0	5.46
	700	14.0			
Hydrogen	5	1.50	2.50	37.8	11.3
	50	15.0			
Hydrogen sulfide	1	0.500	1.00	15.1	7.55
	20	10.0			
Nitrobenzene	3	0.465	0.050	0.756	27.9
	48	7.44			
Tetrachloroethylene	50	1.25	0.10	1.51	9.03
	500	12.5			

n_w = revolutions of the lead screw (rpm),
q_L = volume of material dispensed per lead-screw revolution (ml/revolution),
ρ = density of the liquid (g/ml),
q_D = diluent-gas flow rate (liters/min), and
M = molecular weight (g/mole).

At 25°C and 1 atm, this reduces to

$$C = \frac{(24.5 \times 10^6) \times n_W q_L \rho}{q_D M} . \qquad (66)$$

For gases, the expression is somewhat simpler. Assuming ideality, it is

$$C = \frac{10^6 \times n_W q_G}{q_D} , \qquad (67)$$

where
q_G = volume of gas dispensed per revolution (liters/rev.).
The syringe displacement, $q_{L,G}$, can be calculated from

$$q_{L,G} = \frac{v_S K}{Ln_T} , \qquad (68)$$

where
v_S = volume of the syringe at capacity (ml),
K = factor (25.40 mm/in.),
L = length of the syringe over volume v_S (mm), and
n_T = thread periodicity (threads/in.).

EXAMPLE 27. What motor speed is required to produce a concentration of 50 ppm of carbon monoxide in nitrogen? Assume ideality for both gases. The syringe delivery rate is 75 μl/revolution, and the nitrogen gas is flowing at a rate of 10 liters/min.

$$n_W = \frac{50 \text{ ppm} \times 10 \text{ liters/min}}{10^6 \times (75 \times 10^{-6} \text{ liters/min})} = 6.67 \text{ rpm.}$$

EXAMPLE 28. What is the concentration produced at 25°C and 1 atm when chlorobenzene (density = 1.10 g/ml) is continuously fed at the rate of 12 μl/min into an air stream flowing at 15 liters/min?

$$C = \frac{10^6 \times 24.5 \text{ liters/mole} \times (12 \times 10^{-3} \text{ ml/min}) \times 1.10 \text{ g/ml}}{15 \text{ liters/min} \times 112.6 \text{ g/mole}}.$$

C = 191 ppm.

EXAMPLE 29. What is the concentration produced when perfluorocyclobutane is introduced with a motor-driven syringe at 20 μl/revolution into a stream of ethylene oxide moving at 20 liters/min? The lead screw moves forward at 5 rpm. Use Appendix E to correct for deviations of the gas from ideality.

If the nonideal correction factors for perfluorocyclobutane and ethylene oxide are 1.06 and 0.975 respectively, then the concentration is

$$C = \frac{10^6 \times 5 \text{ rev/min} \times (20 \times 10^{-6} \text{ liters/rev}) \times 1.06}{20 \text{ liters/min} \times 0.975}$$

C = 5.44 ppm.

EXAMPLE 30. What rotation is required to produce a concentration of 1000 ppm of 1,2-dibromoethane (density = 2.16 g/ml) in nitrogen flowing at 1 ft³/min at 20°C and 745 mm Hg? A 5-ml (6.0-cm) syringe is activated by a lead screw containing 28 threads/in.

$$q_L = \frac{5 \text{ ml} \times 25.4 \text{ mm/in.}}{60 \text{ mm} \times 28 \text{ threads/in.}} = 0.0756 \text{ ml/revolution.}$$

$$n_W = \frac{1000 \text{ ppm} \times 28.3 \text{ liters/min} \times 187.9 \text{ g/mole} \times 273°\text{K} \times 745 \text{ mm}}{10^6 \times 0.0756 \text{ ml/rev} \times 2.16 \text{ g/ml} \times 22.4 \text{ liter/mole} \times 293°\text{K} \times 760 \text{ mm}}$$

$$= 1.33 \text{ rpm.}$$

Motor-driven syringes are extremely versatile and several applications include inhalational toxicity studies[141,211,228,133] gas streams mixing with nitrogen dioxide,[206] water,[234] cobalt hydrocarbonyl,[235] aromatic materials,[236] ethanol,[214] nickel carbonyl,[208] and sulfuric acid.[212] They have also been used for checking direct-reading air-quality tubes[237] and instruments,[238] producing air pollution analytical standards[202] and gas mixtures for spectral study,[239] charcoal absorption studies,[217] catalytic feed systems for gas-phase reactions,[240] and generating test and interfering gases.[216]

These systems have the advantages of little or no waste such as seen in the double-dilution techniques. Usually, concentration changes can be made quickly, with the system attaining equilibrium in a few minutes if the dead volume has been minimized. The concentration range of such systems is large and ranges from per cent to parts per million for injected liquids and below 1 ppm for gases. The minimum practical input flow is about 0.1 ul/min.[236] Interface liquids such as water and mercury should be avoided since they only complicate the reservoir-filling operation.

Motor-driven systems are inherently more expensive and can be difficult to build if the necessary parts and shop facilities are not available.[241] The stability and reproducibility at the output concentration should be checked by some alternate technique to ensure best accuracies.

Miscellaneous Injection Methods

There are a variety of alternate methods of injecting trace materials into a dynamic system. These include pistons of gas, mercury, and water activated electrolytically, hydrostatically, gravimetrically, and pneumatically.

Electrolytic Methods

Both gases and liquids can be introduced into a moving gas stream by using the evolved gas or gases from the electrolytic process as the driving force.[124] Acetone and alcohol, for example, have been introduced into an air stream (100 ml/min) at the rate of 1 μl/min using 89 μA and the electrolytically evolved gases from water (H_2 and O_2).[242]

Gases generated electrolytically can also be made to control the rate of advancement of a liquid piston that in turn displaces another gas into the system of interest. One such system is shown in Figure 55. Here again, both evolved gases are used to drive a piston of water, oil, or mercury that in turn delivers helium at a constant rate, depending on the current supplied to a moving stream of nitrogen.

The injected gas reservoir can be refilled by reversing the position of the stopcocks and bleeding the helium in slowly under a slight positive pressure. The displacing gas is commonly hydrogen, oxygen, or both, from aqueous sulfuric acid or from potassium

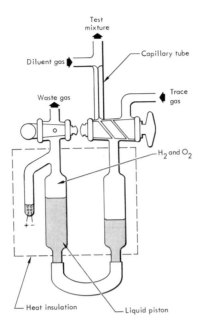

Figure 55. Sketch of a method for injecting gas electrolytically. (Taken from Reference 242.)

sulfate or potassium hydroxide solutions.[61] The entire apparatus should be isolated from temperature fluctuations to prevent irregularities in the gas mixture.

Glass syringes which are actually driven by electrolytically evolved gases are available commercially.[243] They dispense between 0.04 and 4 ml/hr and will run continuously for as long as 10 days while dispensing 1 ml/day on the battery supplied.

Gravity Feed Methods

The pressure created by a column of liquid is sufficient to force a liquid through a restricted opening into the system of interest. Since the rate of flow is a function of the height of the liquid, the reservoir level should change by only a small amount during a given time period in order to maintain uniform introduction of the liquid. Liquid regulation has been achieved using drip regulator clamps[244] or needle valves especially designed for precise flow. Ground-glass stopcocks have been used[226] but are not always successful as flow regulators since the sealing grease is often flushed away. This in turn causes leakage through the stopcock and problems in the system when the grease reappears after the solvents evaporate. This condition can be partially eliminated by using a Teflon stopcock, but precise flow control is still difficult and they should only be used for rough flow adjustments. Direct gravity feed through a capillary has been used,[225,245] but one is limited to just a single flow rate. Micrometer needle valves are generally best since their flow can be adjusted and reproduced with precision.

Gases can be injected by gravity by using the weight of a, ground-glass plunger alone. The plunger's friction with the barrel is minimized by rapid rotation from a tangential blast of air against vanes,[246,247] or a squirrel-cage rotor[248] attached directly to the plunger. The plunger then falls under its own mass at a rate depending on the system pressure, the outlet orifice size, and the nature of the gas.

Liquid and Gas Pistons

Various delivery pistons other than glass and Teflon have been used. Yant and Frey, for example, used a dropping water supply to create a steadily increasing pressure head over a piston of mercury.[241] The mercury in turn displaces the liquid to be vaporized into the mixing chamber. Gases and liquids have also been delivered by dropping mercury to displace gas through a small capillary tube.

Gas pressure is also used to pneumatically activate a moving liquid piston;[61,229,249-251] an example is shown in Figure 56. The contaminant gas is filled through the stopcock until the liquid piston is nearly to the capillary choke. The stopcock is then reversed, and dilution of the trace material proceeds to the right and empties itself. Other variations on this design have been proposed, and one is explained in References 61 and 250.

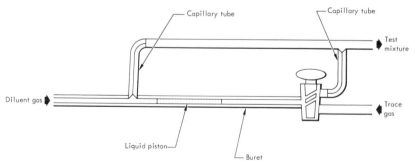

Figure 56. Sketch of a method for injecting gas by means of a liquid piston. (Taken from Reference 250.)

Pulse Diluters

Continuously revolving Teflon stopcocks or the Woesthoff gas-dosing apparatus have been used as a basis of a pulse-dilution system.[157] An example is shown in Figure 57. The trace gas of interest is bled through a rotating stopcock of precisely known volume as shown in Figure 57A. When the stopcock is turned 90 degrees as shown in Figure 57B, the dilution gas purges the stopcock, mixes with more dilution gas, and proceeds to a mixing vessel. The stopcock then returns to position A to be filled while the dilution gas skirts the stopcock through a by-pass and goes to the mixing vessel. Since the gas is added by pulses rather than smoothly and continuously, special care must be taken to mix the gases and ensure that the output mixture is as smooth as possible. With this method, pure gases can be diluted to 50 ppm or less if two or more units are used in series.[252,253] According to manufacturers, this technique can be used with such corrosive gases as chlorine, nitrogen dioxide, and sulfur dioxide since all components in contact with the gas are constructed from Teflon and glass.

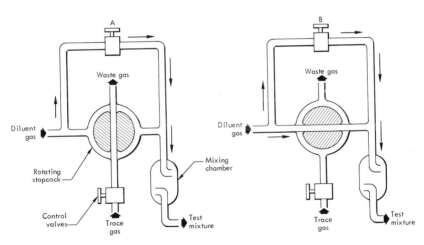

Figure 57. Sketch of a pulse diluter or Woesthoff gas-dosing apparatus.

Axelrod *et al.* have used two such systems in series and report dilutions of 10^8 or better and concentrations from 100 ppm to 0.1 ppb at flows of 30 liters/min.[254] They have further added mixing flasks after each stage to minimize the pulsing concentration created by the nonuniform introduction of the contaminant material into the diluent-gas stream. The major disadvantage is the 3-hour time interval required to reach concentration equilibrium.

Pumps

Liquids and gases can be continuously delivered at low rates from microliters to liters per minute for long time periods. The types of pumps most often used include reciprocal syringe, piston, and peristaltic. The piston type usually involves intermittent flow since no liquid is discharged during the filling stroke, whereas the peristaltic type is continuous and forces the liquid or gas along a pliable tube with mechanical fingers or rollers. Slight variations in the peristaltic sampling rate are still observed from surges caused by the periodic depressing and lifting of the rollers.

Selecting a pump requires knowledge of several variables. Flow-rate range, speed controls, accuracy, working pressure, and constancy of output all play a key role. Several types of commercial devices are summarized in Table XXII, which represents only a randon sampling in a rather extensive field. Flow rates start at 0.1 μl/min and can be furnished at any flow up to liters per second. Usually the stepped-speed, mechanical-gear pumps offer greater accuracy, but they sacrifice versatile speed control. The peristaltic pumps offer a more continuous output, but the flexible lines eventually wear out. Also, because of the various solvent properties of the liquids pumped, the tubing must be interchanged and sometimes recalibrated to ascertain the true flow outputs.

DIFFUSION METHODS

Gases and vapors have the property of diffusing through tubes at a uniform rate if the temperature, concentration gradients, and tube geometry remain unchanged. This phenomenon is a convenient method of producing low concentrations of solvent vapors in a moving gas stream.[255-258] Figure 58 illustrates a typical diffusion system. A metered gas stream is brought to the desired experimental temperature by passing it through a constant-temperature bath. The preconditioned gas then passes over a diffusion tube and mixes with the vapor of interest at a constant rate. The resultant concentration is controlled by varying either the temperature or the flow rate of the primary or the secondary diluent gas.

Diffusion tubes come in a wide variety of configurations, several of which are illustrated in Figure 59. If the diffusion rates are to be calculated, then both the length and the cross-sectional area must be accurately known. The ratio of area to length should be maintained at less than 0.3 for best results.[259] Tubes should be

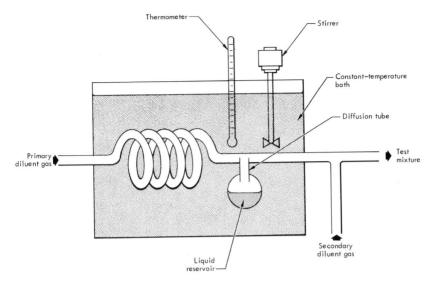

Figure 58. Sketch of a dynamic diffusion system.

between 2 and 20 mm in diameter. Diameters smaller than 2 mm make tube filling a problem, and diameters above 20 mm lead to turbulence, which causes additional errors because of the decrease in the effective diffusion-path length.[260] For these reasons, Types A, B, and C in Figure 59 are preferred because the length does not change as the liquid is consumed.[261-263] If a large reservoir is available, then the diffusion system can be given plenty of time to equilibrate and prolonged runs with the calibrated mixture can be made. Types D and E can be used with success for shorter time periods or else corrected for increasing length.[260,264] If desired, however, automatic, constant-leveling diffusion cells have been designed.[265]

If it is desirable to alter the diffusion rate without changing the diluent-air flow or temperature, then adjustable diffusion cells can be used. In Type F, the effective cross-sectional area is decreased by the partial insertion of a plug affixed to a movable plunger.[263] Type G is controlled by turning the stopcock.[266] However, the most reliable method of controlling the concentration consists of either changing the bath temperature or subsequently diluting the air downstream from the constant-temperature bath. Flow rates past the diffusion tube cannot be indiscriminately chosen and should usually not exceed 1 liter/min.

Diffusion methods offer one of the least complex methods of generating low-concentration analytical standards. Gas mixtures

Table XXII. Characteristics of some low-flow pumps.

Manufacturer	Model No.	Range		Maximum pressure (psig)	Accuracy (% full scale)	Operating principle	Number of speeds	Material pumped
		Minimum (ml/min)	Maximum (ml/min)					
Beckman Instruments, Inc.	74600, -1, -2, -3	0.040	2, 5, 10, 20	2	±2	Cam-actuated valve	Variable	Liquid
Buchler Instruments, Inc.	2-6100	0.04	17	—	—	Peristaltic	Variable	Liquid
	2-6500	0.025	11	—	—	Piston	Variable	Liquid
	2-6000	0.15	15	20	—	Piston	Variable	Liquid
Chromatronix, Inc.	CMP-1	0.04	2.0	500	±0.5	Dual piston	6	Liquid
	CMP-2	0.2	100	100	±0.5	Dual piston	6	Liquid
Clark-Cooper	Labtrol	0.003[a]	90	400 to 1000	±0.25	Reciprocal plunger	Variable	Liquid
Coleman Instruments	102-510	0.05	6	—	—	Peristaltic	Variable	Liquid
Fenet Apparatus & Instrument Company, Inc.	Evenflow	0.05	17	—	—	Peristaltic	Variable	Liquid
Fluid Metering, Inc.	RRM-1	—	1.9, 880	10 to 100	±2.0	Piston	Variable	Liquid
	RRM-2	—	4.3, 1980	10 to 75	±2.0	Piston	Variable	Liquid
	RRP(1 2G		1 6					

Manufacturer	Model				Accuracy	Pump type		Fluid
	1201	0.004				Peristaltic		Liquid, gas
	1204	0.002	251	20	±3	Peristaltic	Variable	Liquid, gas
	1225	0.002	82	—	±3	Peristaltic	30	Liquid, gas
Instrumentation Specialties Company, Inc.	380	0.017	53	50	±1	Piston	18	Liquid
	300	0.083	83	50	±3	Piston	Variable	Liquid
Manostat Corporation	72-895-10	3	5000	91 ft H_2O	±1	Peristaltic	Variable	Liquid, gas
Milton Roy Company	196 series	—	8	1000	±0.3	Piston	Variable	Liquid
Phoenix Precision Instrument Company	4000	0.08	2	1000	±0.5	Piston	Variable	Liquid
Quigley-Rochester, Inc.	59100	0.00013	0.0833	8	±0.1	Reciprocal syringe	24	Liquid
	60100	0.0075	50	8	±0.1	Reciprocal	24	Liquid
Sage Instruments, Inc.	220	0.007	29	—	±0.5	Reciprocal syringe	Variable	Liquid
	212	0.5	270	—	±2	Reciprocal syringe	Variable	Liquid
Sigmamotor, Inc.	T-6S	5	2000	30	—	Peristaltic	Variable	Liquid, gas
	T-8	0.005	60	30	—	Peristaltic	Variable	Liquid, gas
	AL-E	0.009	1	30	—	Peristaltic	Variable	Liquid, gas

[a] Estimated

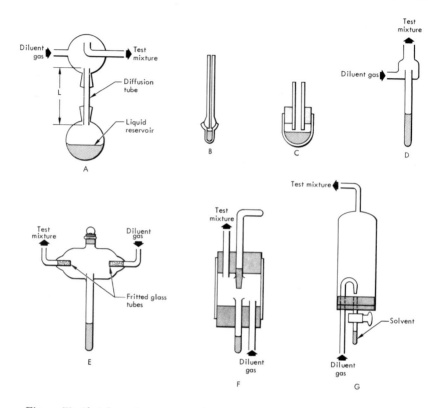

Figure 59. Sketches of some typical diffusion tubes. (A taken from Reference 261, B and C from Reference 263, D from Reference 264, E from Reference 260, F from Reference 263, and G from Reference 266).

can be maintained for extraordinary time periods if the diffusion vessel is large enough. Vapor concentrations from 0.1–100 ppm can be routinely achieved[261] for any substance which can be liquefied in the laboratory. This method is not generally useful when concentrations on the order of 1,000 to 10,000 ppm at relatively high flow rates greater than 10 liter/min are required.

The concentration of a dynamic diffusion system can be expressed by

$$C = \frac{10^6 \times q_d}{Q}, \tag{69}$$

where

$$C = \text{concentration (ppm)},$$

$$q_d = \text{rate of diffusion (ml/min), and}$$

$$Q = \text{flow rate (ml/min).}$$

EXAMPLE 31. What is the resultant concentration of a diffusion system when 5.0 liters/min of air is passed over a tube diffusing 0.200 moles/min in a 32°C constant-temperature bath?

$$q_d = 0.020 \text{ moles/min} \times 22.4 \text{ ml/mole} \times \frac{305°K}{273°K} = 0.500 \text{ ml/min.}$$

$$C = \frac{10^6 \times 0.500 \text{ ml/min}}{5000 \text{ ml/min}} = 100 \text{ ppm.}$$

Assuming that the concentration of vapor at the tube exit is maintained at nearly zero by the dilution air and that the vapor in the tube is saturated,[261] then q_d is usually expressed in moles/sec or g/sec and can be calculated from

$$q_d = \frac{DMPA}{LRT} \ln \frac{P}{P - P_V}, \tag{70}$$

where

q_d = diffusion rate (g/sec),

D = diffusion coefficient (cm²/sec),

M = molecular weight of the diffusing vapor (g/mole),

P = pressure in the diffusion cell (atm),

A = diffusion tube cross-sectional area (cm²),

R = Molar gas constant (ml-atm/mole-K°),

T = absolute temperature (°K),

L = length of the diffusion tube (cm), and

P_V = partial pressure of the diffusing vapor (atm).

If the volumetric flow rate is desired, then Equation 70 reduces to

$$q_d = \frac{DA}{L} \ln \frac{P}{P - P_V}, \tag{71}$$

where q_d is now expressed in ml/sec.

EXAMPLE 32. Determine the A/L ratio when producing 7.50 ppm of chlorobenzene in 2 liters/min of air at 25°C and 1 atm. The vapor pressure and diffusion coefficient of chlorobenzene are 12 mm and 0.0747 cm²/sec respectively. If a maximum diameter of 20 mm is chosen, what tube length will be required?

$$q_d = \frac{7.50 \text{ ppm} \times 2000 \text{ ml/min}}{10^6} = 0.015 \text{ ml/min}.$$

$$\frac{A}{L} = \frac{0.015 \text{ ml/min}}{0.0747 \text{ cm}^2/\text{sec} \times \left[\ln \frac{760 \text{ mm}}{760 \text{ mm} - 12 \text{ mm}}\right] \times 60 \text{ sec/min}}$$

$$= 0.210 \text{ cm}.$$

$$L = \frac{3.14 \times (1 \text{ cm})^2}{0.21 \text{ cm}} = 15 \text{ cm}.$$

Diffusion coefficients at standard conditions (0°C and 1 atm) can be found in the literature,[267] but more current experimental values at 25°C and 1 atm are shown in Appendix F.[268] Diffusion coefficients at other temperatures and pressures can be calculated from the expression

$$D = D_{298}\left(\frac{T}{298}\right)^n \frac{760}{P}, \tag{72}$$

where

D   = experimental diffusion coefficient at a pressure, P, and temperature, T,

D_{298} = the diffusion coefficient at 25°C and 1 atm, and

n   = number of moles.

The value for n, according to kinetic theory, is 1.5, and although experiments indicate that the value is 1.6 to 2.0,[260,269,270] 2.0 is normally used.[271] Also, the diffusion coefficients vary in the literature and many times cannot be adjusted confidently to the experimental range of interest without introducing further error.

EXAMPLE 33. What is the concentration generated when 0.400

liter/min of air is passed over a 50-mm-long tube with a 6-mm diameter containing ethyl alcohol? D_{283} is 0.118 cm²/sec, and the experiment is run at 40°C and 740 mm Hg. The partial pressure of ethanol is 134 mm Hg at 40°C.

$$D_{313} = 0.118 \text{ cm}^2/\text{sec} \times \left[\frac{313°K}{273°K}\right]^2 \times \frac{760 \text{ mm}}{740 \text{ mm}} = 0.159 \text{ cm}^2/\text{sec}.$$

$$q_d = \frac{0.159 \text{ cm}^2/\text{sec} \times 0.283 \text{ cm}^2 \times 60 \text{ sec}/\text{min} \times 2.303}{5.0 \text{ cm}} \log$$

$$\times \frac{740 \text{ mm}}{740 \text{ mm} - 134 \text{ mm}}.$$

$$q_d = 0.108 \text{ ml}/\text{min}.$$

$$C = \frac{10^6 \times 0.108 \text{ ml}/\text{min}}{400 \text{ ml}/\text{min}} = 270 \text{ ppm}.$$

If diffusion coefficients are not available, they can be calculated from Gilliland's approximation,[272] where

$$D = \frac{0.0043 \times T^{3/2} \times \left(\frac{1}{m_A} + \frac{1}{m_B}\right)^{1/2}}{\left(v_A^{1/3} + v_B^{1/3}\right)^2 \times P}, \tag{73}$$

where m_A and m_B are the molecular weights of the diluent and diffusing gases and v_A and v_B are the molar volumes at the boiling point. The molar volume usually chosen for air is 29.9 cm³/g-mole.[273]

Although values of q_d and D can be calculated, theoretical and experimental diffusion rates can exhibit large variations.[260] The complexity of diffusion equations is further increased when such items as minimum diluent-gas flow rate[263] and steady-state equilibrium time are taken into account.[274] It is strongly suggested that other techniques[61] such as gas-chromatographic, infrared, gravimetric, or volumetric determinations be used as a primary calibration if there is any doubt about the system, for the difference between the actual and the theoretical output has been found to be as much as ±10% in error.[259,263,268] In this manner, a plot of the diffusion rate versus the temperature yields a straight line that is easy to use (see Figure 60, for example) and that allows the concentration to be easily and accurately calculated from Equation 57.

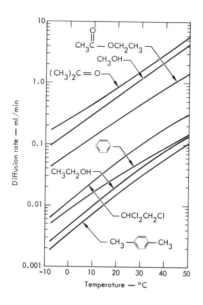

Figure 60. Diffusion rate versus temperature for seven organic liquids (cross-sectional area of the diffusion tube = 0.502 cm², length of the tube = 10 cm, and the pressure = 760 mm Hg).

PERMEATION TUBES

One of the most promising new methods of producing low-ppm concentrations of calibrated gas mixtures involves one of the oldest known phenomena, permeation. Figure 61 shows a schematic diagram of a typical system.[275] The heart of the system is the permeation tube. The gas of interest, compressed to the point of liquefaction, is sealed inside some type of polymeric container. The test gas dissolves in and permeates through the walls of the tube at a constant rate and mixes with the passing diluent gas.

The gases which work best in this type of system are those which have a critical temperature above 20–25°C.[145] The most commonly used are nitrogen dioxide and sulfur dioxide. However, liquids such as benzene and diethyl mercury[276] have been used, and other examples are listed in Table XXIII.

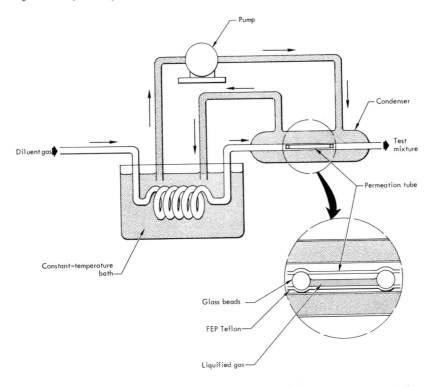

Figure 61. Sketch of a method for dynamically producing gas mixtures with a permeation tube.

A few of the various polymers used in tube construction are shown in Table XXIV. Although many possibilities exist, fluorinated ethylene propylene resin (FEP Teflon) is usually chosen because of its availability and durability.[278] Permeation tubes are available commercially* for about $25.00 each, but experienced personnel can construct them in the laboratory. The liquid or pressurized gas is added to the tube and the ends sealed off with glass beads[276] or stainless-steel balls[278] about 1.5 times the internal tube diameter.

The size of the tube will vary with the concentration sought. The inside diameter of the tube is usually about 1/16 to 1/4 in., and the tube can vary in length from 2–30 cm or longer. Tube life will depend on the temperature of use and storage. Sulfur dioxide tubes last about six months, while nitrogen dioxide and hydrogen

---

*One company, for example, currently supplies SO_2, NO_2, H_2S, butane, propane, benzene, 1-butene, *cis*-2-butene, *trans*-2-butene, and isobutylene.

Table XXIII. Permeation rates of some typical compounds through FEP Teflon.

Compound	Thickness (in.)	Temperature (°C)	Permeation rate (ng/cm/min)	Reference
SO_2	0.012	20 ± 0.5	213	277
SO_2	0.030	20 ± 0.5	138	277
	0.012	20.1	203	278
	0.012	29.1	396	278
NO_2	0.012	13.8	605	278
	0.012	21.1	1110	278
	0.012	29.1	2290	278
Propane	0.012	21.1	53	278
	0.012	29.1	119	278
Butane	0.012	15.5	6.4	278
	0.012	29.1	22.3	278
CHF_2Cl	0.012	20	2.8	278
$CF_3CHClBr$	0.016	93	1.3	278
$CH_2=CHCH_3$	0.030	31	0.29	278
$n-C_5H_{12}$	0.016	93	0.065	278
$C_6H_5CH_3$	0.030	20	0.00006	278

sulfide tubes will last several months if used moderately and stored in a cool place.[285]

Permeation tubes have been best employed to produce standard test-gas mixtures in the parts-per-million range, and they are especially useful as a primary standard for calibrating air pollution analyzers as well as flame photometric detectors at the sub-ppm levels for sulfur dioxide, carbon disulfide, methyl mercaptan, and hydrogen sulfide in air.[286]

The permeation of gas through polymeric materials is basically a diffusion process that occurs because of the concentration gradients between the inner and outer surfaces of the membrane wall. The quantity of gas, q_d, diffusing through the boundaries of the tube as expressed by Fick's law is

Table XXIV. Properties of some polymer films used in permeation tubes.

Material	Trade name	Thickness (in.)	Reference
Fluorinated ethylene propylene resin	FEP Teflon	0.030	275, 277
Fluroinated ethylene propylene resin	FEP Teflon	0.012	277
Fluorinated ethylene propylene resin	FEP Teflon	0.001	279
Polyethylene	—	0.027 to 0.526	280
Polyethylene	Alathon	0.025	281
Polyethylene	—	0.001 to 0.037	282
Polyvinyl acetate	—	0.135 to 1.332	283
Polyvinylidene chloride	Saran Wrap	0.025	281
Polyamide	Nylon 6	0.113	281
Polyester	Mylar	0.031	281
Polyethylene terephthalate	Mylar	0.00031 to 0.006	282
Polythene	Diothene	0.0635 to 0.0254 mm	284

$$q_d = DSA \frac{P_1 - P_2}{L} = p_G A \frac{P_1 - P_2}{L} \qquad (74)$$

where

A = membrane area,

D = diffusion constant,

S = solubility constant of the gas in the membrane,

L = film thickness,

$P_{1,2}$ = total pressures on each side of the membrane wall, and

p_G = gas permeability constant.

The gas permeability constant, p_G (p_G = DS), is a function of the temperature, the gas characteristics and the membrane properties, and it is mostly pressure-independent.[287,288]

The permeability is given by the classical expression

$$p_G = p_G^o \, e^{-E_P/RT}, \qquad (75)$$

where

p_G^o = a constant,

E_P = permeation activation energy,

R = molar gas constant, and

T = absolute temperature.

In any permeation tube system with a fixed geometry, all of the variables should remain essentially constant except for the temperature, which governs the permeation rate exponentially.

Equations 74 and 75, although usually valid over the temperature range of interest, are not generally used to compute the concentration of standard test mixtures. Instead, permeation rates are determined gravimetrically at the experimental temperatures desired. A representative plot of permeation rate versus temperature is shown in Figure 62.[278] After an initial waiting period to allow the tube to equilibrate, the tubes are weighed, stored in a desiccator at a known temperature, and reweighed after several days. Care must be taken to make the weighings under the same conditions of humidity, for absorbed water can give false apparent weights. A semimicrobalance is normally used for best accuracy since the weight losses are usually on the order of milligrams. Table XXIII shows some examples of typical permeation rates.

Permeation tubes can also be calibrated volumetrically, using the microgasometric technique shown in Figure 63. A flask housing the permeation tube is attached to a compensated Warburg syringe manometer and brought to temperature equilibrium in a

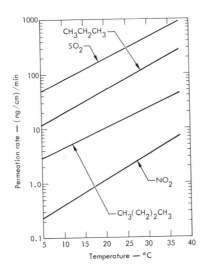

Figure 62. Permeation rate versus temperature for four organic gases.

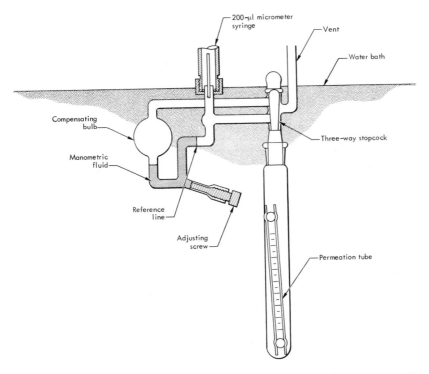

Figure 63. Sketch of a microgasometric apparatus for determining permeation rates. (Taken from Reference 289.)

water bath. The meniscus of the manometer fluid (n-nonane when calibrating sulfur dioxide tubes) is brought just to the left of the reference line. As gas permeates through the tube walls and pushes the meniscus to the reference line, a timer is started. After a certain time interval (2 hours or less), the micrometer screw is repeatedly readjusted and the volume and timer readings noted. The permeation rates can then be calculated knowing the volume and pressure and applying a gravimetric temperature correction.

The concentration, C, generated from a given permeation tube can be calculated from the expression

$$C = \frac{(22.4 \times 10^6) \times \dfrac{T}{273°K} \times \dfrac{760 \text{ mm}}{P} \times p_R}{QM} , \quad (76)$$

where

T = temperature of the system (°K),

P = pressure of the system (mm Hg),

p_R = permeation rate (g/min),

Q = flow rate of the diluent gas (liters/min), and

M = molecular weight of the permeating material (g/mole).

EXAMPLE 34. What flow rate of air is required to produce a concentration of 2 ppm of sulfur dioxide in air at a room temperature and pressure of 25°C and 1 atm respectively? The permeation rate at 25°C is 300 ng/min/cm for a 6-in. tube.

$$p_R = 6 \text{ in.} \times 2.54 \text{ cm/in.} \times 300 \text{ ng/min/cm}$$

$$= 4.57 \text{ } \mu g/min.$$

$$Q = \frac{(22.4 \times 10^6) \times (4.57 \times 10^{-6} \text{ g/min}) \times 298°K}{2 \text{ ppm} \times 64.1 \text{ g/mole} \times 273°K}$$

$$= 0.872 \text{ liter/min.}$$

Permeation tubes offer several unusual advantages over their dynamic counterparts. The low degree of complexity and low range (0.2 to 200 ppm)[285] make them ideal for field instrument calibration and laboratory standards. High precision and an accuracy of ±1%[278] can be obtained if the proper temperature control (±0.1°C) is maintained. If a temperature control of ±0.02°C is maintained, an average deviation of ±0.5% from 1.00 ppm of SO_2 has been reported.[290] Some undesirable characteristics do exist, however. There are relatively few materials which permeate fast enough to be useful at even a low flow rate. Liquids tend to diffuse so slowly (10^{-5} to 10^{-7} μg/cm/min) that they are below the useful range. Also, temperature control is so critical that a difference of ±1% can cause an error of ±10% in the expected concentration produced.[291] If the best accuracy is to be achieved, relatively expensive temperature-control systems should be used.

Each tube used must be gravimetrically or volumetrically calibrated only after it is in equilibrium with its environment. Immediately after manufacture, the stresses of sealing cause the tubes to exhibit differences in permeation even at the same temperature. Therefore, it is desirable to wait several days after filling before weighing. Often, long periods of time must pass before calibration because of the small weight losses on the order of milligrams. The relative humidity must be as similar as possible during both gravimetric determinations, for absorbed moisture will yield false permeation rates.

Usually, only liquefiable materials can be used with permeation tubes, and even gases such as carbon dioxide and nitrogen dioxide have been known to weaken and rupture the walls of the tubes.[254] Usually, tubes can be stored in the refrigerator when not in use to prolong the useful tube life. However, it has sometimes been observed that cooling the tube in low temperatures and then reheating it to the experimental conditions produces some sort of thermal hysteresis and invalidates the expected permeation rate.[279]

EVAPORATION METHODS

Evaporation techniques comprise one of the most generally useful dynamic methods. The diluent gas is passed in close proximity to the liquid to be vaporized by either dispersing it through or passing it over the liquid of interest. The gas stream can be saturated and further diluted, but partial saturation can be used and indeed is usually most desirable. The diluent gas can also be passed through a volatile solid as well as a liquid.

The classical types of evaporation units are shown in Figure 64. Usually, a two-piece vessel with a capacity of 100 ml to 2 liters and connected by a ground-glass joint is chosen. The gas normally enters through a centrally located gas-dispersion tube and is dispersed into minute bubbles, the size of which depends on the tube porosity. Dispersion tubes, shown in Figure 65, are available in the arbitrary porosity designations of extra fine, fine, medium, coarse, and extra coarse. The finer the porosity, the greater the pressure required to force the gas through the tube and the better the efficiency of evaporation. The amount of liquid evaporated will depend on the bubble size, the rate of ascent, the temperature of the liquid, and the height of the liquid column as well as its boiling point and viscosity. Small-volume bubblers with replaceable dispersion tubes (Figure 64F) have also been specially designed.[74]

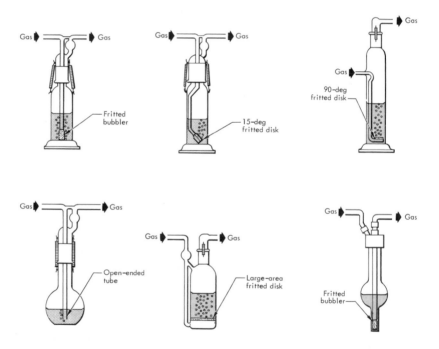

Figure 64. Sketches of six typical gas-dispersion bottles.

The rate of evaporation will slowly decrease with time as the liquid is carried away and the column of liquid above the dispersion tube slowly recedes. This can be minimized by attaching a large auxiliary tank or eliminated all together by using a reservoir of the type shown in Figure 66. Hence, if the gas pressure in the dispersion bottle remains constant, which it should at a given flow, liquid from the reservoir will flow to the bubbler as it is

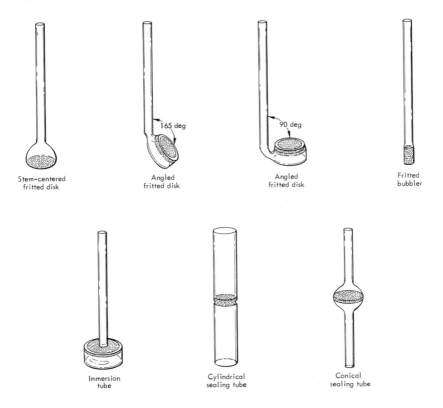

Figure 65. Sketches of seven kinds of gas-dispersion tubes.

needed[292] until the pressure difference between the bubbler and the reservoir just equals the pressure exerted by the difference in the liquid heights.

The dispersed gas is seldom saturated with liquid even at reduced flow rates and with extra-fine gas dispersion apparatus. Saturation will only occur if condensation like that shown in Figure 67 occurs. The carrier gas is swept over hot, refluxing vapors, up the vertical condenser, and further diluted with diluent gas. The glass vessel assists in the smooth evaporation of the solvent, for without it flowmeter oscillations are routinely observed, making precise dilution difficult.

If the total-saturation method is not used, the bubbler should be enclosed in a constant-temperature bath since the vapor pressure of the solvent is directly dependent on the temperature. As the solvent evaporates, the liquid cools, causing a rapid decrease in the vapor output. A circulating constant-temperature bath will help ensure more uniform evaporation and reduce the time required to reach temperature equilibrium.

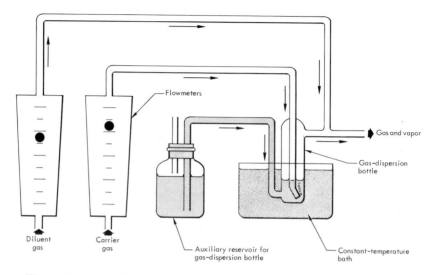

Figure 66. Sketch of a constant-level evaporation unit with an auxiliary reservoir.

Production of contaminants in air streams is often initiated by bubbling pure nitrogen through the material. This prevents further oxidation and chemical reactions caused by prolonged contact with oxygen in the air. The partially saturated stream of nitrogen is then diluted with air. Contaminated air streams of 1,1-dimethyl hydrazine,[293,294] trichloroethylene,[295,296] acetic acid,[297] nitro olefins,[293,298] carbon disulfide,[299] phosphorous halides,[300] and tributyl phosphene[301] are just a few examples which may be prepared using this type of system.

Usually, liquid mixtures cannot be evaporated simultaneously because the mole fraction of the vapor phase is quite different from the mole fraction of the liquid phase unless a minimum-boiling azeotropic solution is present. Such azeotropes are useful for handling reaction systems of hydrofluoric acid[302-304] and formaldehyde.[302] Nevertheless, gases dissolved in very heavy liquids can be used as the volatile liquid with only the gas being selectively removed from solution. Trimethylborane[305] and phosgene[306] dissolved in oil are prime examples.

Gas streams totally saturated with vapor from low-boiling materials are not normally used because of the explosive hazard and because the high concentrations require extensive dilution of mixture if the ppm range is desired. Some saturated systems such as water vapor[307] and mercury (see Chapter 6) in air have been successful, however. The carrier or diluent gas should be purified

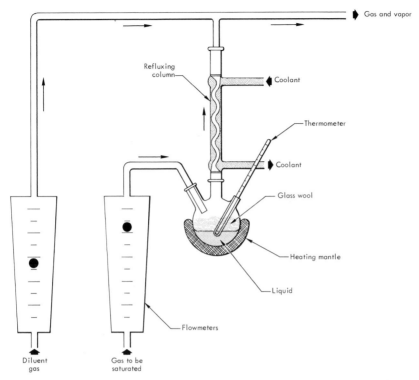

Figure 67. Sketch of the apparatus used to produce saturated vapor mixtures via condensation.

and free from dust, oil mists, water, and other organic materials. Such materials will disperse the solvent, altering its evaporative characteristics.

Evaporation methods have been used for checking analytical methods,[296,301,308-310] animal- and human-inhalation studies (see References 293, 295, 299, 300, 305, 311–313) and effects-on-vegetation experiments,[302] but they have found only limited use in producing standards for gas-phase analysis. The method is excellent for adding a single volatile liquid to a gas stream, but it has the major disadvantage that the effluent gas mixture itself must be independently analyzed by some alternate analytical method. The usual methods which have been employed include gravimetric and polarographic,[314] flame-ionization,[295] conductometric,[297] and spectrophotometric[315] techniques.

The concentration achieved by a carrier-gas stream which is only partially saturated can be determined by

$$C = \frac{(22.4 \times 10^6) \times \dfrac{T}{273°K} \times \dfrac{760 \text{ mm}}{P} \times W}{M q_D \tau}, \quad (77)$$

where

C = average concentration produced (ppm),

T = experimental temperature (°K),

P = experimental pressure (mm Hg),

W = weight lost from evaporation vessel (g),

M = molecular weight (g/mole),

q_D = flow rate of diluent gas (liters/min), and

τ = time required to evaporate weight W (min).

at 25°C and − 1 atm, Equation 77 reduces to

$$C = \frac{(24.5 \times 10^6) \times W}{M q_D \tau}. \quad (78)$$

EXAMPLE 35. What is the concentration generated if 0.56 g of benzene is evaporated into a stream of oxygen flowing at 0.10 ft ^{3}/min? The time required for evaporations is 20 min, and the oxygen is maintained at 0°C and 2 atm.

$$C = \frac{(22.4 \times 10^6) \times \dfrac{1 \text{ atm}}{2 \text{ atm}} \times 0.56 \text{ g}}{78.0 \text{ g/mole} \times 0.1 \text{ ft}^3/\text{min} \times 28.3 \text{ liters/ft}^3 \times 20 \text{ min}}.$$

C = 1421 ppm.

Concentrations may also be calculated directly from vapor-pressure data if it is certain that the diluent-gas stream has reached theoretical saturation at a known temperature. If the total pressure, P, is expressed as the sum of the partial vapor pressures at a specified temperature, then

$$P = p_a + p_b + \cdots + p_n. \quad (79)$$

The concentration in per cent by volume is then

$$C = \frac{10^2 \times p_n}{P} . \tag{80}$$

Expressed in parts per million, this becomes

$$C = \frac{10^6 \times p_n}{P} . \tag{81}$$

The vapor pressure exerted by a liquid at a given temperature is also directly obtainable from the relationship

$$\log p = A - \frac{B}{C + t} , \tag{82}$$

where

$$p \quad = \text{ vapor pressure (mm Hg),}$$

$$t \quad = \text{ temperature (°C), and}$$

$$A, B, C = \text{ constants characteristic of each liquid.}$$

The constants A, B, and C are experimentally determined and are tabulated in Appendix G for a few of the more common liquids.

EXAMPLE 36. Calculate the vapor pressure of bromocyclohexane at 25°C.

$$\log p = 7.3414 - \frac{1778.8}{235 + 25} = 0.4999.$$

$$p = 3.17 \text{ mm Hg.}$$

EXAMPLE 37. What is the concentration of dimethyl formamide if it saturates a stream of nitrogen gas at 40°C and 1.0 atm? Express the concentration in per cent.

$$\text{Log } p = 7.3438 - \frac{1624.7}{216.2 + 40} = 1.0023.$$

$$p = 10 \text{ mm Hg.}$$

$$C = \frac{10^2 \times 10 \text{ mm}}{760 \text{ mm}} = 1.32\%.$$

EXAMPLE 38. An air flow is saturated with acetone and is diluted 10-fold by further downstream dilution. At what temperature must the saturation unit be held to maintain the effluent concentration at 3000 ppm? The total pressure of the system is 620 mm Hg.

$$C = 10^2 \times 3000 \text{ ppm} = 3.0 \times 10^5 \text{ ppm}.$$

$$p = \frac{CP}{10^6} = \frac{(3.0 \times 10^5 \text{ ppm}) \times 620 \text{ mm}}{10^6}.$$

$$p = 186 \text{ mm Hg}.$$

$$t = \frac{-B}{(\log p_a) - A} - C.$$

$$t = \frac{-1161}{(\log 186) - 7.0245} - 224.$$

$$t = 20°C.$$

These calculations provide only a rough estimate of concentrations as they really exist in the experimental test apparatus, and errors of ±15% are not uncommon, especially when working with the more volatile materials in saturated gas streams. Better success is noted when working with liquids whose partial pressures are less than 1 mm Hg, for the amount of evaporated material is so small that temperature equilibrium and large-scale dilution are much less of a problem.

ELECTROLYTIC METHODS

Many gases can be synthesized on a laboratory scale using electrolytic or coulometric methods. This method has long been used in anaytical chemistry to electrodeposit metal ions from solution. The gases which are normally evolved in side reactions are of special interest in producing several types of dynamic systems.

The electrolysis of any solution takes place when enough potential is applied to two electrodes mutually arranged in a solution so that current can flow. As the voltage across the solution is raised from zero, a significant current increase is noticed at a certain point (the decomposition potential), and the amount of gas evolved from that point on is theoretically a linear function of the applied potential. The electrodes, normally constructed from an inert metal such as platinum, either are deposited with a metal ion from solution or evolve a certain gaseous species depending on the electrolyte employed. The gas generated can then be subsequently mixed with some diluting carrier gas, and a mixture of known concentration is thus produced.

Selection of an appropriate electrolyte involves the consideration of four requirements as outlined by Hersch *et al.*[242] First, no side reactions must occur at the electrode of interest. This can be avoided by assuring that a completely pure and plentiful supply of electrolyte is maintained. There must be more electrolyte at the electrode than can be potentially used, or serious deviation from expected gas-evolution rates will be observed.

Second, gases at the other electrode, if they will interfere, must be diverted from the carrier-gas stream. This can usually be done by shaping the reaction vessel in the form of a U and having the unwanted materials sent to the atmosphere as shown in Figure 68. Another alternate method of electrode separation is the use of a stopcock sealed with a highly conductive electrolyte such as sulfuric acid as shown in Figure 69. A 45-V battery will drive several milliamperes through such a stopcock. If the arrangement shown in Figure 44 is used, the unwanted gas can be suppressed entirely. For example, oxygen will not be evolved at the anode of a platinum-screen electrode buried in a bed of active carbon. Other examples are cited by Hersch *et al.*[242,316] If both gases produced from the electrodes do not interfere with one another, then an electrolysis cell of the type shown in Figure 70 can be employed.[242]

Third, the time to attain equilibrium concentration should be minimized. This can be accomplished within seconds if the electrode is either in the shape of a thin vertical platinum wire emerging from an inverted glass "icicle" as shown in Figure 69 or hanging down with a glass bead fused to the tip as shown in Figure 71. The solution level should only contact about 1 mm of exposed electrode wire. This configuration favors the almost immediate saturation of the surrounding solution so that the diluent gas thus receives all of the evolved gas.

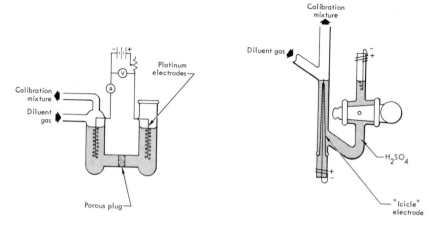

Figure 68. Sketch of a U-shaped electrolytic reaction vessel in which the unwanted gas generated by the right-hand electrode is vented to the atmosphere.

Figure 69. Sketch of an electrolytic reaction vessel with an "icicle" electrode.

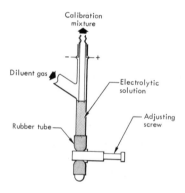

Figure 70. Sketch of an electrolytic reaction vessel with unseparated electrodes. Both generated gases are combined in the diluent gas. The adjusting screw is used to adjust the level of the electrolyte.

Fourth, the concentration produced should be as smooth as possible. If the electrode is small and if at least a 45 volt battery is used, small, barely visible bubbles should be continuously generated. The smallest current provided should not be lower than $10\,\mu A$ since smooth gas evolution then becomes difficult.[242] Excess heating caused by high currents (above 0.5 A) must be avoided as

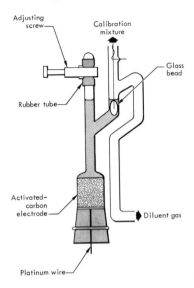

Figure 71. Sketch of an electrolytic reaction vessel with an activated-carbon
electrode. The glass bead provides fast
equilibrium times.

well. Examples of various types of electrolytic systems are shown
in Table XXV. The arsine and stibine methods discussed by Saltzman[77] are particularly useful.

The concentration of gas mixtures produced electrolytically are
based on calculations using a variation of Faraday's law,[187] which
states that

$$I = \frac{znF}{\tau} = zFq_E,\qquad(83)$$

where

$I \;=\;$ current (A),

$z \;=\;$ number of electrons required to liberate 1 mole of gas,

$n \;=\;$ number of moles liberated,

$F \;=\;$ Faraday's constant (96,489 Coul/mole),

$\tau \;=\;$ time (sec), and

$q_E \;=\;$ rate of gas production (moles/sec).

Table XXV. Some common electrolytic systems.

Gas desired	Electrolyte and electrodes	Gas produced from alternate electrode	Reference
AsH_3	Pt, $Na_3AsO_3 + H_2SO_4$, Pt	O_2	18, 77
$SbH_3 + H_2$	Pt, $KSbC_4H_4O_7$, Pt	O_2	18, 77
$O_3 + O_2$	Pt, H_2SO_4, Pt	H_2	242, 316-320
$C_2H_6 + CO_2$	Pt, CH_3CONa, Pt	H_2	321
Cl_2	Pt, NaCl, Pt	H_2	242, 316
NO	Pt, $NOHSO_4 + H_2SO_4$, Pt	O_2	61, 322
NO_2	Pt, $NOHSO_4 + H_2SO_4$, Pt	—[a]	61, 322, 323
O_2 (H_2)	Pt, H_2SO_4, Pt Pt, K_2SO_4, Pt Pt, KOH, Pt	H_2 (O_2)	242, 316
O_2 (H_2)	Pt, $H_2SO_4 + Hg_2SO_4 + C$, Hg Pt, H_2O, C Pt, KOH + HgO + C, Hg Pt, KOH + CdO, Cd	None	242, 316
N_2	Pt, $N_2H_4 + HCl$, Pt Pt, $N_2H_4 + H_2SO_4$, Pt	H_2	61, 242, 316 324
Air	Pt, $N_2H_4 + HCl$, Pt[b] Pt, KOH, Pt[b]	H_2	61
D_2	Pt, $K_2SO_4 + D_2O$, Pt	O_2	242, 316
CO_2	Pt, $H_2C_2O_4$, Pt Pt, $CH_3CO_2Na + HCO_3^-$, Pt	H_2	61, 242, 316 325
T_2	Ni, KOH + TOH, Ni	O_2	61

[a]Both gases evolved react chemically to form NO_2.

[b]Two separate electrolytic cells. The anodic gases N_2 and O_2 are generated and mixed in a 4:1 ratio.

The concentration, C, produced in parts per million when diluted with a carrier gas having a flow rate, q_D is

$$C = \frac{10^6 \times q_E}{q_D} = \frac{10^6 \times I}{zFq_D}, \qquad (84)$$

where q_D is also measured in moles per second. If 1 mole of gas contains 24,060 ml at 20°C and 1 atm, and if the current, I, is expressed in milliamps, then Equation 84 becomes

$$C = \frac{1 \times 10^{-3} \text{ A/mA} \times 24{,}060 \text{ ml/mole} \times 60 \text{ sec/min} \times 10^6}{zq_D \times 96{,}489 \text{ Coul/mole} \times 10^3 \text{ ml/liter}}$$

$$= \frac{14.96 \text{ I}}{zq_D} , \qquad (85)$$

where

$\quad$ C $\quad$ = $\qquad$ concentration (ppm),

$\quad$ I $\qquad$ = $\qquad$ current supplied (mA), and

$\quad$ q_D $\quad$ = $\qquad$ diluent-gas flow rate (liters/min).

EXAMPLE 39. What is the concentration in ppm of carbon dioxide produced when 200 μA are supplied to a solution of oxalic acid at room temperature and pressure? The flow rate of the diluent gas is 0.300 liter/min, and the anode reaction is $C_2O_4^= = 2CO_2 + 2e^-$.

$$C = \frac{14.96 \times 0.200 \text{ mA}}{2 \times 0.300 \text{ liter/min}} = 5.0 \text{ ppm.}$$

EXAMPLE 40. What current must be supplied to a solution of sodium chloride to produce a concentration of 1 ppm Cl_2 in nitrogen flowing a 1 ft³/min? The anode reaction is $2Cl = Cl_2 + 2e^-$

$$I = \frac{1 \text{ ppm} \times 2 \times 1 \text{ ft}^3/\text{min} \times 28.3 \text{ liters/ft}^3}{14.96}$$

$$= 3.78 \text{ mA.}$$

Electrolytic processes many times do not proceed as theoretically planned. Usually, a correction or yield factor, N, must be inserted to make Equation 85 valid.

$$C = \frac{14.96 \times I \text{ N}}{zq_D} . \qquad (86)$$

If conditions other than 20°C and 1 atm are maintained for both the diluent and the electrolytically produced gases, no temperature or pressure correction is needed. Thus, the concentration is a ratio of the two corrected gas flow rates. However, if conditions change in the electrolytic cell, but a corresponding change is not felt by the diluent gas, the Equation 86 becomes

$$C = \frac{14.96 \times I \ N}{z q_D} \left(1 + \frac{T - 293°K}{293°K} + \frac{760 \ mm - P}{760 \ mm} \right) . \quad (87)$$

EXAMPLE 41. What current is required to produce a concentration of 10 ppm of AsH_3 in 1.00 liter/min of nitrogen? The yield factor is 45%, and the cell temperature is 35°C at 1 atm. The cell reaction is $AsO^{3-} + 9H^+ + 6e^- = 3H_2O + AsH_3$.

$$I = \frac{10 \ ppm \times 6 \times 1 \ liter/min}{0.45 \times \left(1 + \frac{15°}{293°} \right) \times 14.96} = 8.48 \ mA.$$

The electrolytic method of adding trace contaminations has the advantage of producing very low concentrations with the flick of a switch. It requires no moving parts, but the construction of some systems requires the services of a first-rate glass blower. Small electrolytic units are not generally available commercially and are somewhat complicated. The small volumes generated (a few microliters per minute) make this an ideal method of checking instruments where continuous low-ppm concentrations are needed, but many trace contaminants cannot be produced by electrolysis or in sufficient volumes to be useful in the per cent range of concentration. If a particular reaction of interest is desired but has not been well investigated, the yield factor must be checked with some alternate method to ensure reliability since the factor is affected by electrode discoloration, electrolytic impuriites, and insufficient electrolyte.

CHEMICAL METHODS

Controlled addition of a contaminant gas to a moving gas stream can be accomplished with chemical reaction techniques. If the material of interest is unstable, extraordinarily reactive, commercially unavailable, or prohibitively expensive, it may be desirable to continuously produce certain types of gases on a small scale in the laboratory. Such reactions are of the type usually encountered in organic and inorganic chemistry and include recombination, catalytic and thermal decomposition, rearrangement, and photochemical dissociation in both gas and liquid phases.

The apparatus involved is almost as diverse as the number of possible reactions themselves and usually involves either a gas-liquid or a gas-solid reaction system. Figure 72 illustrates a method of continuously producing nitrogen dioxide in a gas-liquid system. A metered stream of nitric oxide is bubbled into a solution of acidified permanganate solution, and nitrogen dioxide is generated by the reaction

$$3NO + 2HMnO_4 \rightarrow 3NO_2 + 2MnO_2 + H_2O. \quad (88)$$

As the nitrogen dioxide bubbles to the surface in the reaction flask, it is swept away by an appropriate diluent gas, normally nitrogen. A desiccant filter may be provided to remove unwanted water vapor from the calibration gas mixture. If desired, further dilution can be accomplished downstream from the filter. The system must equilibrate for several hours before it can be used because of the solubility of the resultant nitrogen dioxide in the permanganate solution and because of the adsorption of some of the NO_2 on the filtering material.

An example of a gas-solid system is shown in Figure 73.[18,77] Chlorine gas, diluted by air, is passed over sodium chlorite to produce chlorine dioxide by the reaction

$$Cl_2 + 2NaClO_2 \rightarrow 2ClO_2 + 2 NaCl. \quad (89)$$

A number of possibilities for using reaction systems are tabulated in Table XXVI, but only a few have been practiced.[61] As noted, the additive may be an oxidative, reductive, or a catalytic gas, liquid, or vapor. Table XXVII lists some additional reactions that have been tried. Ozone as produced for irradiation of oxygen by UV light is a particularly useful reagent and is discussed more fully in Chapter 6.

Most of the calculations covered in this chapter can be applied to systems involving chemical reactions. A few examples follow.

EXAMPLE 42. At what rate must hydrogen be passed over heated nickelous chloride to produce a concentration of 5.0% hydrogen chloride when diluted with air flowing at 10 liters/min? Assume that the gases are mixed at room temperature and that the conversion reaction of hydrogen chloride proceeds stoichiometrically to completion according to the equation in Table XXVI.

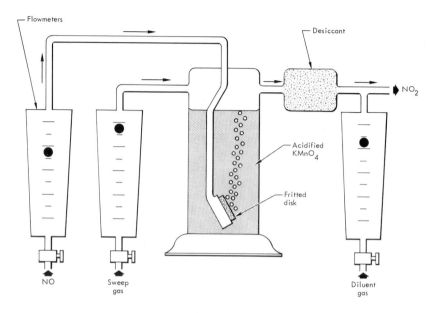

Figure 72. Sketch of an apparatus for continuously producing NO_2 from NO and $KMnO_4$.

From Equation 57,

$$q_{HCl} = \frac{Cq_{air}}{1 - C} = \frac{0.050 \times 10 \text{ liters/min}}{1 - 0.05}$$

$$= 0.53 \text{ liter/min.}$$

$$q_{H_2} = 0.53 \text{ liter/min} \times 0.5 = 0.26 \text{ liter/min.}$$

EXAMPLE 43. Cyclohexene is injected and evaporates into a moving stream of nitrogen at the rate of 1.2 g/hr. It is subsequently transferred to a heated chamber, where it is converted quantitatively to 1,3-butadiene according to the equation in Table XXVII. What is the concentration generated if the nitrogen is flowing at 1.0 ft³/min? Assume a room temperature and pressure of 21°C and 760 mm Hg. The volume of cyclohexene produced per minute is found from Equation 66.

$$C = \frac{24.1 \times 10^6 w}{VM} = \frac{24.1 \text{ liters/mole} \times 1.2 \text{ g/hr} \times 10^6}{1.0 \text{ ft}^3/\text{min} \times 28.3 \text{ liters/ft}^3 \times 54 \text{ g/mole} \times 60 \text{ min/hr}}.$$

$$C = 316 \text{ ppm.}$$

Table XXVI. Conversion reactions.[a]

Reactants		Products
C_2H_5OH	$\xrightarrow{Al_2O_3}$	$C_2H_4 + H_2O$ (in N_2)
C_6H_5OH	$\longrightarrow$	$CO + 5C + 3H_2$ (in N_2)
$Fe(CO)_5$	$\xrightarrow{200°C}$	$5CO + Fe$ (in N_2)
$2H_2 + O_2$	$\xrightarrow{Pt}$	$2H_2O$
$C_{10}H_8 + 12O_2$	$\longrightarrow$	$10CO_2 + 4H_2O$
$Cl_2 + H_2$	$\xrightarrow{UV}$	$2HCl$
$R \cdot NH_2 + H_2$	$\xrightarrow{Ni}$	$RH + NH_3$ (in N_2)
$O_2 + 2C,$	$\longrightarrow$	$2CO$ (in N_2)
$H_2O + C$	$\longrightarrow$	$CO + H_2$ (in N_2)
$H_2 + Ag_2S$	$\xrightarrow{500°C}$	$H_2S + 2Ag$ (in N_2)
$H_2 + NiCl_2$	$\xrightarrow{600°C}$	$2HCl + Ni$ (in N_2)
$H_2 + 2CoF_3$	$\xrightarrow{300°C}$	$2HF + 2CoF_2$ (in N_2)
$6H_2O + Mg_3N_2$	$\longrightarrow$	$2NH_3 + 3Mg(OH)_2$
$6H_2O + Al_2S_3$	$\longrightarrow$	$3H_2S + 2Al(OH)_3$
$3H_2O + Al(OR)_3$	$\longrightarrow$	$3ROH + Al(OH)_3$
$HCl + Na_2S_2O_5$	$\longrightarrow$	$SO_2 + NaHSO_3 + NaCl$
$2CF_3COOH + CaC_2$	$\longrightarrow$	$C_2H_2 + (CF_3COO)_2Ca$
$2Cl_2 + N_2H_4 \cdot H_2SO_4$	$\longrightarrow$	$4HCl + H_2SO_4 + N_2$
$Cl_2 + C_6H_4(OH)_2 \cdot Kr^{85}$	$\longrightarrow$	$Kr^{85} + C_6H_4O_2 + 2HCl$[b]
$Cl_2 + 2NaClO_2$	$\longrightarrow$	$2ClO_2 + 2NaCl$
$SO_2 + 3NaClO_2$	$\longrightarrow$	$2ClO_2 + NaCl + Na_2SO_4$
$3NO + 2CrO_3$	$\xrightarrow{200°C}$	$3NO_2 + Cr_2O_3$
$3NO + 2HMnO_4$ (aq)	$\longrightarrow$	$3NO_2 + 2MnO_2 + H_2O$

[a] Data taken from Reference 61.

[b] Electrolytic chlorine liberating beta-emitting krypton from quinol clathrate.

157

Table XXVII. Additional reactions used to produce calibrated gas and vapor mixtures.

Reactants	Products	Reference
$4H^+ + 2NO_2^- + 2I^- \longrightarrow$	$I_2 + 2NO + 2H_2O$	326
$NO + O_3 \longrightarrow$	$NO_2 + O_2$	327
$NaF + H_2O \longrightarrow$	$HF + NaOH$	302, 387
$H_2SO_4 + 2NaF \longrightarrow$	$2HF + Na_2SO_4$	124
$2AlP + 3H_2O \longrightarrow$	$2PH_3 + Al_2O_3$	328
$3O_2 \xrightarrow[h\nu]{UV}$	$2O_3$	Chapter 6
$H_2C_2O_4 \xrightarrow[h\nu]{UV}$	$CO + CO_2 + H_2O$	61
$HCOOH \xrightarrow[H_2SO_4]{\Delta}$	$CO + H_2O$	30, 124, 140
$2NO + O_2 \longrightarrow$	$2NO_2$	Chapter 6
$2Pb(NO_3)_2 \xrightarrow{\Delta}$	$4NO_2 + 2PbO + O_2$	331, 332
$C_5H_5NHCo(CO)_4 + H^+ \longrightarrow$	$HCo(CO)_4 + C_5H_5NH^+$	235, 333
$KCN + H_2O \longrightarrow$	$HCN + KOH$	77
$2KCN + H_2SO_4 \longrightarrow$	$2HCN + K_2SO_4$	334
$(CH_3)_2CO \xrightarrow{\Delta}$	$CH_2 = C = O + CH_4$	335
$\bigcirc \!\!\!\! | \; \xrightarrow{\Delta}$	$CH_2 = CHCH = CH_2$ $+ CH_2 = CH_2$	335

Although the chemical reaction technique seems straightforward enough, especially in the classical sense, a number of difficulties arise. The reactant feed mechanisms required are normally more complex than the usual dynamic system since often two or more reactants are required in the gas phase or some carefully regulated reaction vessel must be provided when liquids are used. Characteristically, the rate of reaction is a logarithmic function of temperature, and the usual rule of doubling the reaction rate with every 10°C rise in temperature applies.

Although the number of reactions available is practically limitless, two factors must be considered before selecting an appro-

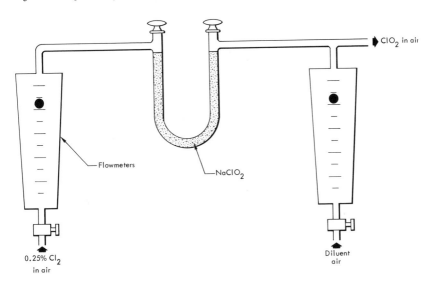

Figure 73. Sketch of an apparatus for continuously producing ClO_2 from Cl_2 and $NaClO_2$.

priate reaction. First, are the products formed within a reasonable length of time after mixing, and second, does the reaction proceed stoichiometrically to completion? The rate of most reactions can be found in the literature from experimentally determined reaction-rate constants, and it is expressed in moles per unit time. The degree of quantitative completion (*i.e.*, the ratio of products to reactants) is also an experimental quantity given by the equilibrium constant. If the reaction system under study does not proceed to completion, or if doubt exists as to the character of the effluent gases and vapors, then further painstaking and time-consuming analysis is required to assay the true nature of the calibrated gas mixtures.

As expected, many reactions which produce a selected contaminant also produce additional products or generate unwanted side reactions. These by-products, along with any unreacted starting material, must be removed selectively by filtration, absorption, or adsorption, which further complicates the system.

It is desirable, except in a few selected instances, to purchase the gas of interest either in its pure form or diluted by an inert gas. Then the gas can be assayed and further diluted as necessary via the conventional, commercially available flowmetering devices.

Chapter 6

Specialized Systems

There are several materials which must be considered separately when formulating procedures for both the static and the dynamic methods of producing gas and vapor mixtures. Because of their unusual reactivities, toxicities, vapor pressures, or calculation considerations, they must be treated as special cases. Several systems are described briefly — nitrogen dioxide, ozone, diatomic halogens, hydrogen cyanide, mercury, and water vapor.

OZONE

The production of ozone must be done dynamically if continuous, constant, and reproducible mixtures with a diluent gas are to be achieved. This is due primarily to ozone's extraordinary reactivity and its decomposition to oxygen upon standing. If static systems are attempted, the experimenter quickly discovers that the concentration decays from one-third[146] to as much as one-hundredth[315] of the initial concentration, depending upon the circumstances.

Methods of Generation

Ozone is produced by a variety of methods, and the most common include ultraviolet illumination and electric discharge, although electrolytic techniques have been tried.[317] Ozone may also be obtained commercially in a semipurified state.

Probably the most preferred method of laboratory ozone production is the use of ultraviolet irradiation,[336-345] an example of

161

which is shown in Figure 74. Air or oxygen is admitted to the chamber at a known rate, where the oxygen is partially converted to ozone with an ultraviolet lamp. The mixture is then further diluted and the test mixture is ready for use. The concentration of ozone can be varied by adjusting the air flow or by altering the input voltage to the UV lamp with a variable transformer. The UV lamp should be run for several hours to allow for stabilization. In some cases, it is desirable to mount the UV lamp outside the chamber. If this is done, a quartz-walled chamber must be used to permit entry of the radiation, and concentration changes can be effected with a movable slide.[343,346]

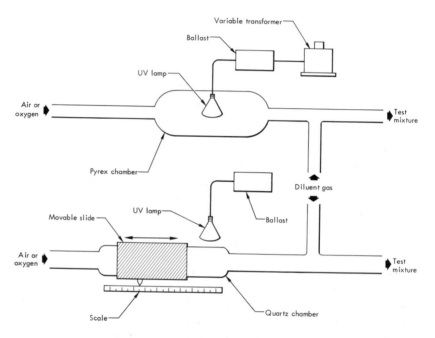

Figure 74. Sketch of two systems for continuously generating ozone with an internal (top) and an external (bottom) ultraviolet lamp.

All downstream apparatus should be glass or Teflon since these materials have the least effect on ozone.[338] If polyethylene or polyvinyl tubing must be used, then connections should be as short as possible. Rubber tubing should be scrupulously avoided.

The other major method of ozone production is the electrical discharge.[347-351] The kinetics and mechanism of this method have been discussed extensively.[352] Usually, a silent discharge is preferred[353] because actual spark discharges produce excessive quantities of nitrogen oxides, which constitute a primary interference in many ozone analyses. Figure 75 shows a typical system.[354] Oxygen is passed between two concentrically oriented electrodes separated by Teflon spacers. The electrodes are activated with a high-voltage transformer (a 10–15-kV neon-sign transformer is usually sufficient). A rheostat alters the ozone concentration by appropriate adjustments. An electrostatic precipitator functions on the same principle except that the high-voltage output is usually rectified, but it can also be used as an ozone production unit.

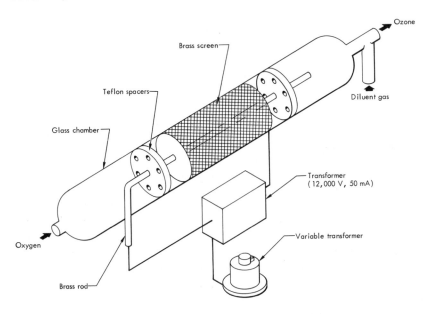

Figure 75. Sketch of an apparatus for generating ozone using a silent discharge.

Ozone can be purchased commercially in liter-sized stainless-steel cylinders. It is obtained as 8-mole % in the liquid phase, with the balance being an inert gas, usually Freon 13 ($CClF_3$). This method, however, has three serious drawbacks. First, the decomposition of ozone to oxygen as shown in Figure 76 is extremely rapid above −20°C; hence, the shelf life is limited. Second, if the ozone is withdrawn as a vapor, the concentration gradually decreases due to the presence of its oxygen decomposition product. Thus, the ozone must be expelled from inverted cylinders as a liquid. This necessitates the use of large dilutions to achieve the concentrations normally needed for experimental work, especially in animal-toxicology and air-pollution studies. Third, ozone, especially in such a highly concentrated form, is an

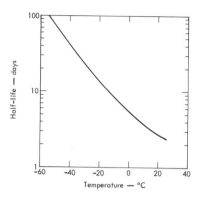

Figure 76. Half-life of ozone versus temperature. Ozone decomposes to liquid oxygen.

extremely powerful oxidant and can detonate alone or with a variety of other fuels.

Methods of Analysis

Although ozone mixtures can be generated in the ppm range, there is no absolute method of predicting with accuracy the concentration of ozone produced. System geometry, gas flow rates, and the intensity of the arc discharge or ultraviolet lamp all influence the final concentration. It is therefore necessary to analyze the gas mixture at the various experimental conditions encountered. Once this is accomplished, the conditions, when duplicated, will usually produce the expected predetermined ozone concentration.

There are numerous wet-chemical and instrumental methods available. Most of these are reliable when dealing exclusively with ozone, but many methods deviate sharply from the expected values in the presence of numerous interfering gases. Nitrogen dioxide, hydrogen sulfide, and sulfur dioxide are a few examples of such interferences. If, however, only ozone and its mixtures with air are encountered, this lack of specificity is no longer troublesome.

The methods commonly in use include potassium iodide (both wet chemical and coulometric),[337,340,355] phenolphthalein, fluorescein, diacetyldihydrolutedine,[356] rubber decomposition,[341] polymer chain scission,[182] detector tubes,[357] and a host of others. The most widely used and generally accepted wet-chemical method is the potassium-iodide method. Ozone in the air, when bubbled through a neutral iodide solution, reacts as follows:[358]

$$O_3 + H_2O + 2I^- = I_2 + 2OH^- + O_2. \qquad (90)$$

In an excess of potassium iodide,

$$I_2 + I^- \rightarrow I_3^-. \qquad (91)$$

The concentration can then be determined spectrophotometrically by the intensity of the triiodide ion at 352 mμ. In an alkaline solution, a somewhat different reaction takes place.[358]

$$3O_3 + I^- \rightarrow 3O_2 + IO_3^-. \qquad (92)$$

When acidified,

$$IO_3^- + 6H^+ + 8I^- \rightarrow 3I_3^- + 3H_2O. \qquad (93)$$

The phenophthalein[359] and fluorescein[360] methods are extremely sensitive, but there is some question as to the reaction stoichiometry[354] at low concentration. Other wet-chemical techniques include sodium diphenylamine sulfonate,[261] 4,4'-dimethoxy-stilbene,[399] and the nitrogen-dioxide-equivalent method.[75]

Several instrumental methods are available for continuously measuring ozone concentrations.[342,362] One method involves applying a small potential across the electrodes that in turn is influenced by the reaction of ozone drawn through a potassium-iodide solution as shown in Equation 90. Hydrogen, formed at the cathode, then combines with the iodine produced by ozone oxidation of the iodide. As ozone enters the system, a current is produced which is directly proportional to the ozone concentration. Such instruments have a full-scale deflection of 100 pphm with reported sensitivities of $\pm$1 pphm. Additional performance criteria are given by Potter and Duckworth.[363]

At least two other alternative techniques exist to continuously monitor ozone concentration—chemiluminescent and clathrate analyses. In the chemiluminescent method, the gas sample is drawn over a material containing Rhodamine B, which in turn is viewed with a sensitive photocell.[344,364,365] The ozone causes the material to emit a quantity of light proportional to its concentration. The response and sensitivity of this technique are extremely high, but must also be checked against a known standard ozone mixture to determine the light output-concentration relationship. The clathrate method, on the other hand, can be used to measure extremely low concentrations directly. Ozone, passing over Kr[85] (containing quinol clathrate) releases radioactivity[366] and is subsequently measured. The ozone oxidizes the quinol to quinoline, which in turn liberates the krypton[367] as follows:

$$(C_6H_4(OH)_2)_3 \cdot Kr^{85} + O_3 \rightarrow 3C_6H_4O_2 + 3H_2O$$
$$+ Kr^{85}. \tag{94}$$

This technique can be used to measure concentrations on the order of one part per ten billion or less.[367] However, the method is limited by its relatively long response time.

Galvanic monitoring of ozone can also be achieved by using bromide as the principal electrolytic constituent.[345] The ozone and bromide interact in the following manner:

$$O_3 + 2\ Br^- \rightarrow O_2 + O^{-2} + Br_2. \tag{95}$$

$$2e^- + Br_2 \rightarrow 2\ Br^-. \tag{96}$$

$$C + O^{-2} \rightarrow CO + 2e^-. \tag{97}$$

The anode reaction represents the oxidation of the relatively large charcoal electrode. This method has the advantage of using no applied potential and of continuously reusing and regenerating the electrolyte almost indefinitely.

NITROGEN DIOXIDE

Nitrogen dioxide and its mixtures with other gases, usually air, are commonly required in low concentrations, especially in air pollution studies. There are, however, several problems which make accurate and precise production of such a test atmosphere somewhat difficult to control and maintain.

One of the primary difficulties when handling nitrogen dioxide is its propensity for dimerizing by the reversible reaction

$$2NO_2 \rightleftharpoons N_2O_4. \tag{98}$$

As expected, both temperature and pressure affect this equilibrium. Some typical results showing the contribution of each variable over the usual range of interest are shown in Figure 77. This graph was constructed from the equilibrium constants given by Verhoek and Daniels.[368] For example, a sample of pure nitrogen dioxide taken at 40°C and 1 atm would contain 58% N_2O_4 and 42% NO_2. There are numerous other values given for the dissociation constants and heats of vaporization that are involved in these calculations, which would cause the N_2O_4/NO_2 ratio to be shifted slightly.[369-371]

A further difficulty with NO_2 is its boiling point of 21.3°C. Many times it is desirable to conduct experiments at room temperature. The experimenter will sometimes find his nitrogen dioxide alternating between the gas and liquid phases if the room temperature is in the neighborhood of 20°C.

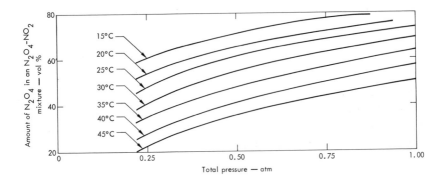

Figure 77. Dimerization of NO_2 versus pressure at seven isotherms.

Static Systems

Known concentrations of nitrogen dioxide can be prepared in closed vessels either by direct addition or by a chemical reaction within the vessel. If direct addition is used, then Figure 77 must be used to estimate and compensate for the partial dimerization.

EXAMPLE 44. Estimate the equilibrium volume of NO_2 required to produce a concentration of 5 ppm in a 40-liter vessel. Room temperature and pressure are 25°C and 1 atm.

$$V_{NO_2} = 5 \text{ ppm} \times 40 \text{ liters} \times 10^{-5} = 200 \ \mu l.$$

Figure 77 shows that nitrogen dioxide is about 74% N_2O_4 and 26% NO_2 at the experimental conditions. Therefore, 1 μl of the mixture contains the equivalent of 1.74 μl of NO_2. Hence, the indicated volume of NO_2 required is 200 μl/1.74 μl = 115 μl.

If concentrations are produced by the syringe injection method, they should be checked by one of the available analytical methods to ensure their accuracy.

Concentrations of nitrogen dioxide can also be conveniently prepared by chemical reaction. Oxidation of nitric oxide (NO) by air can be used if high concentrations are desired or if the nitric oxide is first reacted with oxygen[372,373] and subsequently injected into the system of interest. Low-ppm concentrations are not usually created by direct injection of pure nitric oxide because of the relatively slow rate of reaction.[77,139,374] This reaction rate is normally considered third order,[375] but if the initial oxygen concentration is sufficiently high and does not change appreciably even as the reaction nears completion, it becomes second order.[376]

$$\frac{d(NO_2)}{d\tau} = -K(NO)^2, \tag{99}$$

where K, the rate constant, is 3×10^{-4} ppm/min.[377] Figure 78 illustrates the reaction process with time. Note that even after 1 hr only 15% of an initial concentration of 10 ppm of nitric oxide has reacted to form nitrogen dioxide.

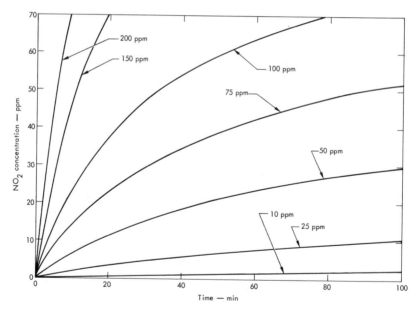

Figure 78. Concentration of NO_2 versus time at seven initial NO_2 concentrations.

The thermal decomposition of lead nitrate has also been used successfully,[139,372] reacting according to the following equation:

$$2Pb(NO_3)_2 \rightarrow 2PbO + 4NO_2 + O_2. \qquad (100)$$

Figure 79 shows the apparatus required to operate such a system. Known weights of reagent-grade lead nitrate crystals are placed between glass-wool plugs. The chamber is partially evacuated and the lead nitrate is heated with a small burner. When the brown nitrogen dioxide becomes evident, a slight amount of diluent gas is allowed to enter and sweep the evolved gases into the chamber. This process is repeated several times until no more nitrogen dioxide is, evident, even after extensive heating. If desired, a combustion-tube furnace may be substituted as a heat source with a maximum temperature of about 450°C.[332] The test chamber is then brought back to atmospheric pressure.

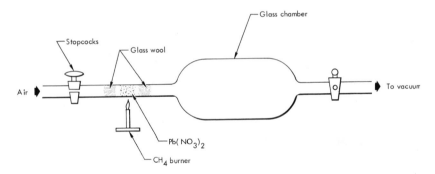

Figure 79. Sketch of an apparatus for producing static NO $_2$ mixtures in air by decomposing lead nitrate.

EXAMPLE 45. What weight of lead nitrate is needed to produce 10 ppm of nitrogen dioxide in a 100-liter static chamber? Assume room temperature (21°C) and pressure (1 atm).

From Equation 44,

$$W_{NO_2} = \frac{10 \text{ ppm} \times 100 \text{ liters} \times 46 \text{ g/mole}}{24.1 \text{ liters/mole} \times 10^6}$$

$$= 0.00191 \text{ g.}$$

If equation 100 proceeds to completion, then

$$W_{Pb(NO_3)_2} = \frac{0.00191 \text{ g} \times 0.5 \times 331 \text{ g/mole}}{46 \text{ g/mole}}$$

$$= 0.00687 \text{ g.}$$

Dynamic Systems

Nitrogen-dioxide concentrations in the ppm range can be generated by most of the methods outlined in Chapter 5 only if preliminary dilution is made to obtain a usable stock mixture. Any attempt to meter the pure gas at normal cylinder pressure and room temperature or to produce mixtures by single or double dilution will usually meet with little or no success. Pure nitrogen dioxide, however, has been pressurized with helium to 25 psig, metered as a liquid, and later vaporized.[378] If continuous-flow dilutions are to be made, usually stock mixtures of 1 and 0.5% in nitrogen have been used before a subsequent air dilution.[77,193,379] Asbestos-plug flowmeters can be successfully used to produce nitrogen dioxide mixtures,[75,78] but the pure substance must again be diluted to prevent fouling of the plug.[18] Motor-driven syringes have also been used to dispense a previously diluted amount of nitrogen dioxide.[216] Permeation tubes have also been used effectively in producing concentrations in the parts-per-million range (see Chapter 5).

An interesting method of producing nitrogen-dioxide mixtures has been done electrolytically by Shaw.[323] There seems to be no suitable reaction to evolve NO_2 directly, but NO is easily generated quantitatively by the electrolysis of nitrosyl hydrogen sulfate ($NOHSO_4$) dissolved in concentrated sulfuric acid at a platinum cathode under an atmosphere of nitrogen by the following reaction:

$$NO^+ + e^- = NO. \tag{101}$$

The anode reaction produces oxygen from the sulfate by the reaction:

$$2SO_4^= = S_2O_7^= + 1/2\ O_2 + 2e^-. \tag{102}$$

If the oxygen and nitric oxide are allowed to mix before dilution for a sufficient time interval, the nitrogen-dioxide yield is almost quantitative.

Another, lesser known method of generation involves the reaction of nitric oxide with excess ozone[327] by the following reaction:

$$NO + O_3 \xrightarrow{K_1} NO_2 + O_2 \qquad (103)$$

where $K_1 = 1.17 \times 10^{10}$ ml/mole-sec. Additional by-products such as nitrogen pentoxide are formed, but they, along with excess ozone, can be thermally decomposed by passing the gas mixture through a chamber filled with glass beads and heated to 150°C. Using such a system to determine nitric oxide by an ultraviolet-absorption technique, Singh *et al.* varied the concentration from 100 to 5000 ppm with a reproducibility from about 10% at low concentrations to about 3% at high concentrations.[327]

Methods of Analysis

Diluted stock gas mixtures made commercially must be checked in the laboratory to determine the initial concentration and re-checked periodically to ensure that the nitrogen dioxide is not slowly decomposing or being adsorbed on the cylinder walls.

Most analytical methods for nitrogen dioxide in the ppm range are achieved through some type of spectrophotometric analysis. Even if galvanic devices are used to continuously monitor a moving gas stream,[380] they are also calibrated normally using some colorimetric method.[78,381]

The analytical technique usually chosen is one devised by Saltzman.[216] The gas sample is bubbled through a dilute acetic acid solution containing sulfanilic acid and N-(1-naphthyl) ethylenediamine dihydrochloride. The nitrogen dioxide diazotizes the sulfanilic acid, which forms an azo dye upon coupling with the dihydrochloride. The color intensity is proportional to the nitrogen dioxide in accordance with Beer's law and is usually read at 500 mμ. Standards are made from solid sodium nitrite, with 2.03 μg being the equivalent of 1 μl of nitrogen dioxide at 25°C and 1 atm. Nitric oxide can be bubbled through an acidified permanganate solution, converted to nitrogen dioxide, and subsequently determined in the same manner.[382]

MERCURY

Mercury is a most unusual metal because of its relatively high vapor pressure (10^{-3} mm Hg at 20°C), and it requires special techniques to produce known concentrations with accuracy. Methods using motor-driven syringes are inadequate because of the low injection rates involved and the difficulties of subsequent volatilization.

Mercury is one of the few materials which lends itself readily to the evaporation method of generating test atmospheres. Basically, this entails saturating the gas of interest with mercury by raising and lowering the temperature and diluting the subsequent test gas to achieve the concentrations desired.[383,384] A diagram of such a system using air as a test gas is shown in Figure 80.

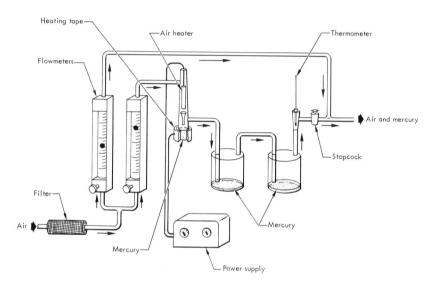

Figure 80. Sketch of an apparatus for dynamically generating mercury vapor.

Compressed air passes through indicating silica gel, soda lime, and a charcoal filter to remove any impurities. The purified air stream splits into two lines. One line goes through a flowmeter (about 40 liters/min maximum) and is subsequently used as the dilution air. The other line flows through a lower-range flowmeter (about 1 liter/min maximum) into the saturation unit. Needle valves built into the flowmeters govern the flow rate in each line.

A ceramic-core heater heats the air in the saturation unit, and the heater wires, soldered to Kovar seals, yield gas-tight connections. The heated air flows through a 2-mm opening and impinges on the surface of mercury warmed (to about 60°C) with a heating tape. Variable transformers control the temperature of the tape and the air heaters.

The mercury-laden air then travels to two 100-ml equilibrium vessels. The air cools rapidly, and any excess mercury condenses on the mercury already present in the bottles. The air becomes saturated with mercury during this period. After the air passes from the equilibrium bottles, an accurate temperature is taken with an ASTM-23C thermometer (18–28°C range). The saturated and dilution air are then combined, and the test mixture is ready for use.

A stopcock placed after the thermometer provides an easy method of discontinuing the flow of mercury vapor and also facilitiates checking for leaks in the saturation unit. No flow should be observed in the low-flow flowmeter when the needle valve is in the fully open position and the stopcock is closed. Various concentrations are made by adjusting the air and mercury-vapor in air dilution ratios at the temperature measured. This temperature should be near ambient temperature if the air flows through the saturation unit at less than 1 liter/min. If the temperature begins to rise rapidly, or if a greater flow rate through the saturator is required, the equilibrium bottles should be enlarged and maintained in a constant-temperature bath for the best results.

An accurate measurement of the temperature is the most crucial part of the calibration operation. Since the vapor pressure of mercury is so dependent on the temperature, an error of 1°C causes a deviation from the expected concentration of 10%. For this reason, the thermometer should not be handled and should be placed as far as possible from the heating equipment.

Concentrations in ppm by volume of the saturated air stream can be calculated from

$$C_{ppm} = \frac{p_{Hg} \times 10^6}{P_A} = \frac{W}{V} \times \frac{22.4 \times \dfrac{T}{273°K} \times \dfrac{760 \text{ mm}}{P_A}}{M_{Hg}} , (104)$$

where

C_{ppm} = concentration by volume (ppm),

p_{Hg} = vapor pressure of mercury (mm Hg),

W/V = weight of mercury per unit volume of air (g/liter),

T = measured temperature of air saturated with mercury (°K),

P_A = atmospheric pressure (mm Hg),

M_{Hg} = molecular weight of mercury (200.6 g/mole).

Substituting in the known values and solving for the concentration in mg/m³, Equation 104 reduces to

$$C_{mg/m^3} = \frac{p_{Hg} \times 200.6 \text{ g/mole} \times 10^6}{P_A \times 22.4 \text{ liter/mole} \times \dfrac{T_m}{273°K} \times \dfrac{760 \text{ mm}}{P_A}}$$

$$= \frac{p_{Hg} \times 3.22 \times 10^6}{T_m} . \qquad (105)$$

The values for p_{Hg} are well known and are shown in Table XXVIII with the calculated saturated air-stream concentration values from Equation 91.

Table XXVIII. Calculated concentrations of air saturated with mercury vapor from 18 to 28°C. [a]

Temperature (°C)	Vapor pressure of mercury (mm Hg)	Concentration of saturated air stream (mg/m³)
18	0.001009	11.2
20	0.001201	13.2
24	0.001691	18.3
26	0.002000	21.5
28	0.002359	25.2

[a] Calculated from Equation 105.

When air dilutes the saturated mercury vapor, Equation 91 becomes

$$C_{mg/m^3} = \left(\frac{q_{Hg}}{q_{Hg} + q_{air}} \right) \left(\frac{p_{Hg} \times 3.22 \times 10^6}{T_m} \right), \qquad (106)$$

where

$$q_{Hg} = \text{flow rate of the mercury-saturated air (liters/min) and}$$

$$q_{air} = \text{flow rate of the dilution air (liters/min).}$$

Table XXIX shows some sample calculations using Equation 106.

Table XXIX. Calculated concentrations of mercury vapor in air.[a]

Flow rate of dilution air (liters/min)	Flow rate of mercury-saturated air (liters/min)	Concentration of mercury vapor (in mg/m^3) at:					
		18°C	20°C	22°C	24°C	26°C	28°C
18.0	0.018	0.011	0.013	0.016	0.018	0.021	0.025
18.0	0.036	0.022	0.026	0.031	0.037	0.043	0.050
14.0	0.050	0.040	0.047	0.056	0.065	0.077	0.090
9.95	0.050	0.056	0.066	0.078	0.091	0.11	0.13
9.9	0.10	0.11	0.13	0.16	0.18	0.22	0.25
9.8	0.20	0.22	0.26	0.31	0.37	0.43	0.50
9.7	0.30	0.34	0.40	0.47	0.55	0.65	0.76
9.6	0.40	0.45	0.53	0.62	0.73	0.86	1.01
8.0	0.50	0.68	0.78	0.92	1.08	1.26	1.48
12.0	0.90	0.78	0.92	1.09	1.28	1.50	1.76
6.0	0.60	1.02	1.20	1.42	1.66	1.95	2.29
6.0	0.67	1.12	1.32	1.56	1.83	2.15	2.52
None	All	11.2	13.3	15.7	18.4	21.5	25.3

[a]Calculated from Equation 106.

HYDROGEN CYANIDE

Because of its extreme toxicity and room-temperature boiling point, hydrogen cyanide is one of the most difficult of all materials to handle in the purified state. It is also dangerous to store for extended time periods, for it sometimes undergoes rapid polymerization, causing sudden, violent explosions. Thus, the shelf life of hydrogen cyanide cylinders is limited. The generation of hydrogen cyamide in the laboratory as it is needed is generally far more acceptable than storing it in large quantities — most of which, in all probability, will go unused.

Static Systems

The classical method of small-scale laboratory production is illustrated in Figure 81. Two reagent reservoirs are made in an ordinary glass test tube by heating the tube to red heat and creating a slight positive pressure within the tube. Excess sulfuric acid is added to one reservoir and a small predetermined volume of sodium cyanide is added to the other as shown in Figure 81A. The end of the tube is then sealed with a torch and inverted as shown in Figure 81B. As the solutions mix, a stoichiometric quantity of hydrogen cyanide gas is liberated into the air space above the mixed solution. Only a small percentage (usually less than 5%) remains dissolved. The glass ampoule can then be transferred to a larger test chamber, broken, and the gas dispersed throughout a larger volume of diluent gas.[385]

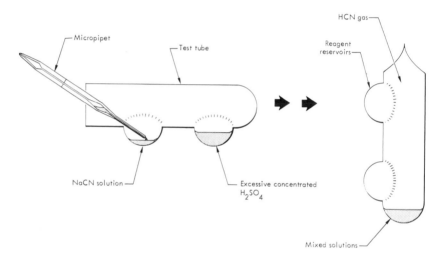

Figure 81. Sketch of an apparatus for producing hydrogen cyanide.

Under static conditions, the concentration of hydrogen cyanide can be determined from a calculation based on Equation 41. If the gas is generated from the reaction of a standard cyanide solution with excess acid, the concentration of hydrogen cyanide is given by

$$C = \frac{v_{HCN} \times 10^6}{v_D} = \frac{v_S c_S RT \times 10^6}{v_D P}, \qquad (107)$$

where

C = concentration (ppm),

V_{HCN} = volume of HCN produced from the acid reaction (liters),

V_D = volume of the diluent gas (liters),

V_S = volume of a standard cyanide solution (liters),

c_S = concentration of a standard cyanide solution (moles/liter),

T = final temperature of the static system (°K),

P = final pressure of the static system (atm), and

R = molar gas constant (0.08205 liter-atm/mole- °K).

EXAMPLE 46. How many microliters of a 1.0-M solution of sodium cyanide, if converted entirely to hydrogen cyanide with excess sulfuric acid, will be required to create a concentration of 100 ppm in a 2-ft³ chamber? The final chamber temperature and pressure are 25°C and 745 mm Hg respectively.

$$V_S = \frac{100 \text{ ppm} \times 28.3 \text{ liters/ft}^3 \times 2 \text{ ft}^3 \times 745 \text{ mm} \times 10^6 \text{ } \mu l/\text{liter}}{1.0 \text{ mole/liter} \times 62.4 \text{ liter-mm/mole-°K} \times 298°K \times 10^6}.$$

$V_S = 227 \text{ } \mu l.$

Dynamic Systems

Continuous generation of hydrogen cyanide can be accomplished by feeding a cyanide salt into an acid at some constant, predetermined rate. This, however, requires a separate reaction vessel, and as the by-products of the reaction accumulate, progressively more hydrogen cyanide remains dissolved in solution rather than being liberated. An alternate method suggested by Saltzman[77] is shown in Figure 82. Air is metered at 0.25 to 0.5 liter/min, and any interfering carbon dioxide is removed with Ascarite. The cleansed air then flows through a condenser and midget impinger containing 30% solution of potassium cyanide. As the air bubbles through, it picks up the hydrogen cyanide from the hydrolyzed cyanide ion and is further diluted with more air if necessary. The water bath and the carrier-gas supply are thermostated at about 29–30°C to stabilize the hydrogen cyanide production. With this technique, an output concentration of 100 ppm can be maintained for up to 10 hours. The hydrogen cyanide produced must be determined analytically, and the colorimetric method by Aldridge[386] is acceptable.[77]

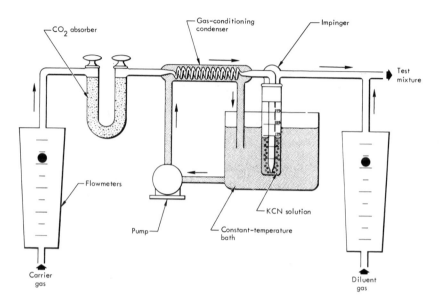

Figure 82. Sketch of an apparatus for dynamically producing hydrogen cyanide by hydrolyzing cyanide ions.

HALOGEN COMPOUNDS

Halogen compounds comprise the most reactive family of chemical compounds, especially the diatomic species of hydrogen fluoride, bromine, and iodine. A static system involving mixtures with these gases, especially at parts-per-million concentrations, is generally unacceptable because of their great reactivity and adsorption into the chamber walls.

Hydrogen fluoride is one of the most difficult materials to handle in the gas phase, but it can be used or dispersed from aqueous solutions with much less risk. It is commercially available in solutions of 48–51 wt%. Static systems have been used but must be fashioned from inert polymeric materials such as polyethylene or Teflon since hydrogen fluoride reacts rapidly with glass surfaces. Hydrofluoric acid may be added directly to the vessel either as a gas or in the standard or diluted 50% aqueous solution via Teflon syringes. The reaction of sodium fluoride with excess sulfuric acid and its subsequent evaporation has also been used.[124] The desired gas mixture should equilibrate, be withdrawn, and again be added to season the vessel walls and help increase the accuracy of the test-gas mixture. This seasoning is further described in Chapter 4.

Dynamic methods are generally employed for hydrogen-fluoride mixtures. A popular system is outlined in Figure 83.[302,387] Air or the gas of interest is metered through two vessels surrounded by a constant-temperature bath. The first vessel contains water only, while the second contains the selected concentration of aqueous hydrofluoric acid. The preconditioning water vessel helps to stabilize the concentration produced over prolonged time intervals.[302] The temperature of the water bath plays an important roll in the concentrations generated. Hill *et al.*[302] has found that an increase in the bath temperature from 27 to 48°C triples the output of hydrogen fluoride at the same air flow. The output concentration can be monitored electronically with a specific-ion electrode, continuous conductivity meters,[304] or chemically by collecting in 0.1 N sodium hydroxide and performing a subsequent colorimetric analysis using the method of Bellack and Schoubal.[388]

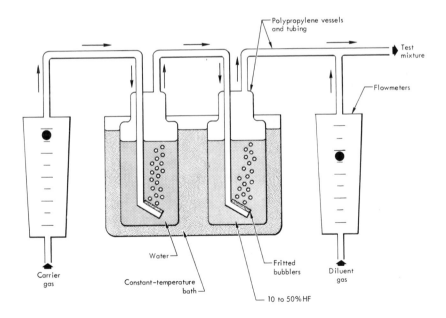

Figure 83. Sketch of an apparatus for dynamically producing hydrogen fluoride.

Other dynamic methods of generation have been proposed. Hersch[61] mentions the continuous conversion of hydrogen passing over cobalt trifluoride at 300°C to produce hydrogen fluoride. Bubbling the gas through a solution of sodium fluoride also produces hydrogen fluoride from hydrolysis. For higher concentrations, gas-stream mixing can be used,[389] but difficulty is encountered in metering and controlling the flow of such a system.

Bromine mixtures have been generated dynamically by bubbling the gas through a solution saturated with bromine[77] as shown in Figure 84. The purified gas is preconditioned to the same temperature as the bromine solution by passing it through a thermostated condenser just before bubbling it through a saturated bromine solution containing excess bromine. If air is used as the carrier gas through a midget fritted tube, an output concentration of 13,000 ppm can be obtained at 26°C and kept constant for many hours.[77] Lower concentrations can be obtained by further downstream dilution. Solubility data for bromine in water is given in Table XXX. Bromine is infinitely soluble in alcohol, chloroform, ether, carbon tetrachloride, and carbon disulfide at room temperature, so saturated solutions cannot be obtained.

Iodine is also difficult to produce in the parts-per-million range of concentration because of its solid nature. The passage of gas

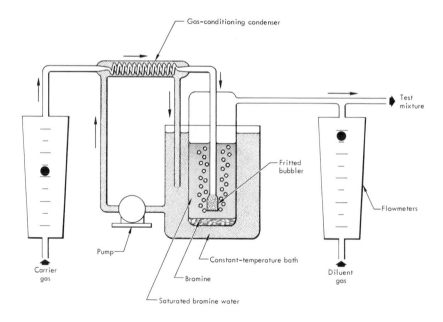

Figure 84. Sketch of an apparatus for dynamically generating bromine.

Table XXX. Solubility of bromine in water.[a]

Temperature (°C)	Solubility (wt %)
0	2.28
3	3.08
5.8	3.73
10	3.60
20	3.41
25	3.39
30.1	3.34
36	3.36
41	3.39
44.8	3.41
48.8	3.45
52.8	3.50
53.6	3.50

[a]Data taken from Reference 390.

over or through the crystals often produces uneven concentrations, even with close temperature control. Reproducibility is often poor since the rate of sublimation is so dependent on iodine grain size. Iodine, however, is partially soluble in a number of solvents, as shown in Table XXXI. As with bromine, the carrier gas of interest can be bubbled through the saturated solution and further diluted downstream with additional carrier gas. Concentration determinations can be done with specific-ion electrodes or one of the numerous colorimetric methods available for this purpose.

Ludwich[326] has proposed a dynamic system for continuous iodine production that is shown in Figure 85. Molecular iodine is generated by the continuous addition of a sodium nitrite solution a drop at a time to sodium iodide dissolved in 3N H_2SO_4 via the reaction

$$4H^+ + 2NO_2^- + 2I^- \rightarrow I_2 + 2NO + 2H_2O. \tag{108}$$

As the iodine is generated, it is swept into the metered diluent air stream by bubbling helium into the reaction mixture. Since some of the iodine remains dissolved in the solution, the exact concentration must be determined by some alternate procedure.

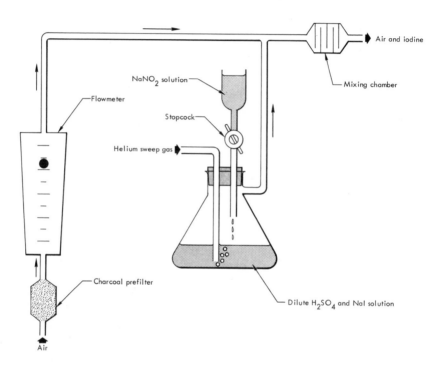

Figure 85. Sketch of an apparatus for continuously producing iodine.

HUMIDITY CONTROL

The production of standard atmospheres with a known humidity is often a requirement in many types of controlled test atmospheres. Test environments for use in plant studies, for example, often require air which is richer in moisture content than the usual dry air present in most laboratory compressed-air supplies. Precision relative humidity control is not always required, but low concentrations of water vapor in air are often needed for precision analytical standards and instrument calibration.

Numerous temperature-controlled humidity chambers are commercially available from almost every scientific supply company. Typically, the humidity ranges obtainable are 20–95% relative humidity over a 3–90°C range. However, specially designed sys-

Table XXXI. Solubility of iodine in various solvents.[a]

Solvent	Temperature (°C)	Solubility
Water	10	0.20% by weight
	20	0.285% by weight
	25	0.335% by weight
	30	0.385% by weight
Carbon disulfide	10	10.51% by weight
	20	14.62% by weight
	30	19.26% by weight
Carbon tetrachloride	15	20.5 g/liter
	18	22.5 g/liter
	21	25.1 g/liter
	25	29.1 g/liter
Chloroform	15	32.6 g/liter
	18	35.4 g/liter
	21	39.5 g/liter
	25	45.2 g/liter
Ethanol	0	16.72% by weight
	25	21.33% by weight
	35	24.60% by weight
Ethyl ether	0	19.34% by weight
	25	25.20% by weight
	35	28.50% by weight
Benzene	25	14.09% by weight
	30	16.10% by weight
Hexane	25	0.456% by weight
Heptane	25	1.702% by weight
	35	2.491% by weight
Toluene	25	3.56 g/liter
Tetrachloroethane	25	4.16 g/liter
Tribromomethane	25	18.96 g/liter

[a]Data taken from Reference 390.

tems can be obtained which operate over a 2–98% relative humidity range.

Constant humidity can also be maintained in a static system by exposing certain saturated aqueous solutions to an enclosed air space at a known temperature.[124] Several of these solutions are tabulated in Table XXXII. In this manner, relative humidity can be maintained from 7–98% at room temperature by varying the saturated solution used.

Table XXXII.   Solutions for maintaining constant humidity.[a]

Relative humidity desired (%)	Temperature (°C)	Saturated solution
98	20	$Pb(NO_3)_2$
95	20	$Na_2SO_3 \cdot 7H_2O$
93	20	$Na_2SO_4 \cdot 10H_2O$
90	20	$ZnSO_4 \cdot 7H_2O$
88	20	K_2CrO_4
86	20	$KHSO_4$
84	20	KBr
81.1	25	$(NH_4)_2SO_4$
79.3	25	NH_4Cl
76	15.5	NaCl
72.7	30	$NaNO_3$
70.8	25	$SrCl_2 \cdot 6H_2O$
66	20	$NaNO_2$
63	30.1	$NaNO_2$
61.4	40	$NaNO_2$
57.9	20.3	$NaBr \cdot 2H_2O$
54	100	NaClO
52	20	$NaHSO_4 \cdot H_2O$
51	80	NaBr
47	20	KCNS
45	20	KNO_2
38	10	$CaCl_2 \cdot 6H_2O$
33	25	$MgCl_2 \cdot 6H_2O$
31	24.5	$CaCl_2 \cdot 6H_2O$
28.4	50	$NaI \cdot 2H_2O$
23.4	90	KF
22.5	25	$KC_2H_3O_2 \cdot 1.5H_2O$
20	20	$KC_2H_3O_2$
15	10	$LiCl \cdot H_2O$
11.1	25	$LiCl \cdot H_2O$
10	20	$ZnCl_2 \cdot 1.5H_2O$
9	24.5	$H_3PO_4 \cdot 0.5H_2O$
7	25	$NaOH \cdot H_2O$

[a]Data taken from Reference 391.

Static and Dynamic Methods

Producing humidities of 5–99% can involve all the usual techniques of dynamic gas-mixture production. Mechanical feed, evaporation, and saturating of air streams all have been used. Figure 86 summarizes some of the more popular techniques involving partial and complete saturation. Figure 86A illustrates the partial saturation-split stream method. The gas of interest is mete-

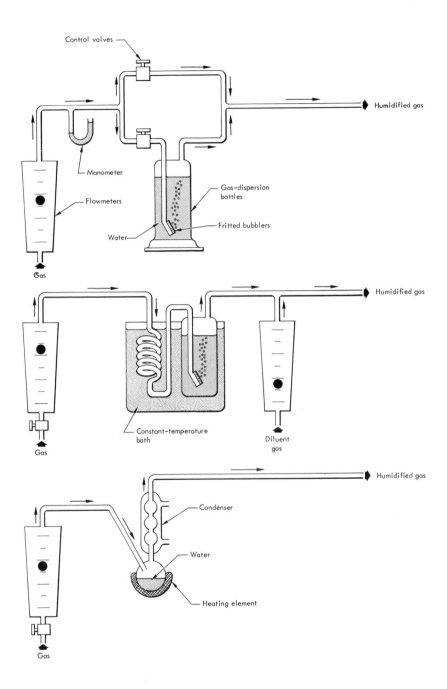

Figure 86. Sketch of three systems for humidifying a moving gas stream via partial saturation with a split stream (top), partial saturation with double dilution (middle), and complete saturation (bottom).

185

red to a T junction where the gas stream is split. One stream is partially saturated, while the other stream is used for a subsequent dilution.[392] Some sort of manometer arrangement must be used since varying the flow rates will effect the pressure of the variable-area flowmeter and usually require a correction factor for the best accuracy.

Figure 86B illustrates the partial-saturation, double-dilution method. In this method, the gas flow rate through the partial saturation unit is adjusted before the flowmeter. Again, a gas-dispersion bottle is useful in assisting in the evaporation of the water. A heated constant-temperature bath surrounding the bottle and the incoming air line greatly increases the maximum relative humidity available. Usually, no manometer is needed since the biggest single pressure drop is caused by the fritted area on the dispersion bottle. However, as time passes and the water level diminishes, the percentage of relative humidity will likewise diminish.

The total-saturation unit shown in Figure 86C is the best way to saturate an air stream in the 90–99% range. Air is metered into a chamber of hot, refluxing, distilled water, cooled to the required temperature with a Graham, West, Allihn, or other suitable condenser, and is ready for further dilution or subsequent trace-contaminant injection. The addition of enough water vapor to totally saturate dry air only increases the volume flow rate by 2–3% at room temperature.

For relative humidities below 1–3% at room temperature, other more exacting methods can be used as shown in Figure 87. A motor-driven syringe or infusion pump can inject at a precise rate a small volume of water. A fine mist is produced by a sprayer or atomizer assembly. Larger droplets can be trapped on extra coarse fritted discs and subsequently evaporated by the passage of the diluent gas. Glass wool can be further added to increase the surface area and assist in evaporation. If higher humidities are desired, or if the water cannot be evaporated fast enough, a source of outside heat, such as a heating tape, is sometimes required to assist in evaporation.

Concentrations in the low part-per-million and part-per-billion range have been prepared by flowing nitrogen saturated with water vapor into an enclosed chamber until a certain specified pressure is reached. Dilution is achieved by further pressurizing the holding tank with dry nitrogen passed through a liquid-nitrogen chiller.[307]

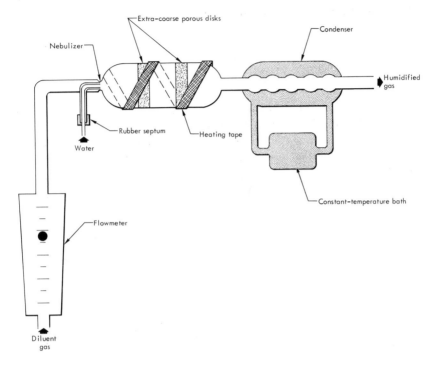

Figure 87. Sketch of an apparatus for humidifying a gas stream with injection.

Calculations

The concentration of water vapor in parts-per-million of dry air can be calculated from partial-pressure data as follows:

$$C = \frac{10^6 \times p_W}{P - p_W}, \tag{109}$$

where

C = concentration (ppm),

p_W = vapor pressure of water (mm Hg), and

P = total pressure of the system (mm Hg).

EXAMPLE 47. What is the concentration of water vapor in air at

20°C and 1 atm? The vapor pressures of water are found in Appendix H.

$$C = \frac{10^6 \times 17.5 \text{ mm}}{760 \text{ mm} - 17.5 \text{ mm}} = 2.36 \times 10^4 \text{ ppm.}$$

EXAMPLE 48. What is the concentration of water vapor present when a stream of nitrogen gas is saturated with water at 73°C and 3 atm and subsequently diluted 100-fold? Use the constants provided in Appendix H for vapor-pressure calculations with Equation 62.

$$\log p_W = 7.9668 - \frac{1668.2}{228 + 73}.$$

$$\log p_W = 2.4246.$$

$$p_W = 265.8 \text{ mm Hg.}$$

$$C = \frac{10^6 \times 266 \text{ mm} \times 10^{-3}}{3 \times (760 \text{ mm} - 266 \text{ mm})} = 179 \text{ ppm.}$$

The concentration of water vapor can also be expressed as the relative humidity, which is the ratio of the quantity of water vapor present to the amount which would saturate the gas at the prevailing temperature. Expressed in terms of partial pressure, this would be[393]

$$H_R = \frac{10^2 \times p_W}{p_{WS}}, \tag{110}$$

when

H_R = relative humidity (%),

p_W = partial pressure of water at temperature T (mm), and

p_{WS} = partial pressure of water at complete saturation at temperature T (mm).

EXAMPLE 49. What is the concentration of water vapor in per cent of wet air and ppm of dry air at 90% relative humidity at 40°C and 1 atm?

The vapor pressure of water at 40°C from Appendix C is 55.3 mm. Hence, the vapor pressure of water at 90% relative humidity is

$$p_W = 0.90 \times 55.3 \text{ mm} = 49.8 \text{ mm}.$$

$$C_{ppm} = \frac{10^6 \times 49.8 \text{ mm}}{760 \text{ mm} - 49.8 \text{ mm}}$$

$$= 7.01 \times 10^4 \text{ parts water per million parts dry air.}$$

$$C_\% = \frac{10^2 \times 49.8 \text{ mm}}{760 \text{ mm}}$$

$$= 6.55\% \text{ water vapor by volume.}$$

EXAMPLE 50. How many grams per minute of evaporated water are required to maintain a relative humidity of 70% in an air stream flowing at 1.00 ft³/min? Atmospheric temperature and pressure are 25°C and 745 mm Hg.

The partial pressure of water at 25°C from Appendix H is 23.8 mm Hg at saturation.

$$p_W = 0.7 \times 23.8 = 16.7 \text{ mm}.$$

$$Q = \frac{16.7 \text{ mm} \times 1.0 \text{ ft}^3/\text{min} \times 28.3 \text{ liters/ft}^3 \times 273°C \times 745 \text{ mm} \times 18 \text{ g/mole})}{(745 \text{ mm} - 16.7 \text{ mm}) \times 22.4 \text{ liters/mole} \times 298°C \times 760 \text{ mm})}.$$

$$Q = 0.469 \text{ g/min.}$$

Humidity is sometimes expressed in per cent, H_p, which is given by

$$H_P = \frac{p_W \times (P - p_{WS}) \times 10^2}{p_{WS} \times (P - p_W)} \qquad (111)$$

and is related to relative humidity by

$$H_P = H_R \frac{P - p_{WS}}{P - p_W}, \tag{112}$$

where P is the total system pressure.

At room temperature, the partial pressure of atmospheric moisture is so small compared with the total pressure that

$$\frac{P - p_{WS}}{P - p_W} = 1, \tag{113}$$

and the per cent of relative humidity and saturation are virtually equal. However, as the temperature is raised and the partial pressure becomes more significant for a given humidity, the numerical difference between saturation and relative humidity becomes more significant.[394]

EXAMPLE 51. Determine the per cent of saturation at 20 and 80°C for air at 50% relative humidity and 760 mm Hg, using Appendix H.

From the appendix, p_{WS} at 20°C is 17.535 mm Hg.

$$H_P = \frac{0.5 \times 17.5 \text{ mm} \times (760 \text{ mm} - 17.5 \text{ mm}) \times 10^2}{17.5 \text{ mm} \times (760 \text{ mm} - 0.5 \times 17.5 \text{ mm})}$$

$$= 49.4\%.$$

$$H_P = \frac{0.5 \times 355.1 \text{ mm} \times (760 \text{ mm} - 355.1 \text{ mm}) \times 10^2}{355.1 \text{ mm} \times (760 \text{ mm} - 0.5 \times 355.1 \text{ mm})}$$

$$= 34.8\%.$$

EXAMPLE 52. Calculate the relative humidity when the temperature of a flowing air stream at 65% relative humidity is raised from 15°C to 75°C.

From the appendix, p_{WS} at 15 and 75°C is 12.8 and 289.1 mm. respectively.

$$H_R = \frac{0.65 \times 12.8 \text{ mm} \times 10^2}{289.1 \text{ mm}} = 2.9\%.$$

Methods of Measurement

Traditionally, the method of continuously monitoring a moving air stream for humidity is wet-bulb psychrometry. In addition, there are electronic methods which can continuously monitor and record the degree of moisture content as either relative humidity or directly as parts-per-million by volume of water vapor.

A wet-bulb psychrometer is shown in Figure 88 and consists basically of two thermometers placed in close proximity. The bulb of one is housed in a wick saturated with water (the wet bulb), while the other (the dry bulb) is left completely open to the gas of interest. The gas, usually flowing past at a velocity of at least 1000 ft/min, cools the wet-bulb thermometer to a new equilibrium temperature. The relative humidity can then be obtained by knowing the dry-bulb temperature and difference between the dry- and wet-bulb temperatures. Such a table is shown in Appendix J, or the data can be obtained from other suitable psychrometric charts.[394]

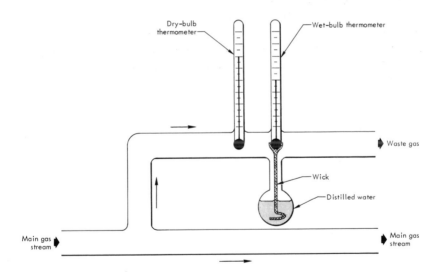

Figure 88. Sketch of an apparatus for continuously measuring humidity using the wet-bulb psychrometric technique.

EXAMPLE 53. Using the table in Appendix J, determine the relative humidity if the dry-bulb reading, t_D, is 21°C and the wet-bulb reading, t_W, is 16.5°C.

$$t_D - t_W = 21 - 16.5 = 4.5°C.$$

From the table, the relative humidity is 64%.

Although this method seems simple enough, there are several disadvantages. In dynamic systems, water must be continuously supplied to the wet bulb to maintain continuous wick saturation. Also, the measuring unit must be placed in a separate gas stream since water evaporating from the wick further adds to the moisture of the gas stream, especially where lower humidities and gas flows are present. For these reasons, it is often desirable to use electronic probes.

Electronic methods, several of which are summarized in Table XXXIII, have the advantage of direct readouts in either per cent of relative humidity or parts per million. The response time is usually less than 2 minutes, with an accuracy of better than ±5% full scale. Most instruments which measure and indicate relative humidity directly are not appreciably sensitive below 5% relative humidity. Most probes must also be used in atmospheres which are free from dusts, moisture droplets, and corrosive gases, all of which cause deterioration of many salt-type sensing devices.

Other hygrometric techniques based on infrared absorption, index of refraction, neutron thermalization, and critical flow have been evaluated by Hollander *et al.*[395] Cole[396] has described and evaluated several techniques involving saturated-salt solutions, Dunmore elements, and electrolytic and piezoelectric sorption systems.

Table XXXIII. Characteristics of several humidity and water-vapor detection devices.

Manufacturer	Probe construction	Range[a]	Interferences	Response time	Accuracy	Temperature range
Hygrodynamics, Inc.	LiCl/LiBr, Pt electrodes	3 to 100% RH	Dust, polar compounds, sulfides, mercury, acids, halogens	0.15 min	±1.5%	-20 to 140°F
American Standard, Inc.	Permeable glass	1 to 100% RH	Can be cleaned with water	10 min	±2%	0 to 500°F
Kahn & Company, Inc.	P_2O_5 film, Pt electrodes	1 to 1000 ppm	—	—	±5%	0 to 80°C
CEC/Analytical Instruments	P_2O_5 film	1 to 1000 ppm	Amines, NH_3, alcohols, unsaturated hydrocarbons, F_2, HF	2 min	±5%	0 to 125°F
Cambridge Systems, Inc.	Pt resistance thermometer in a chilled copper sensor	-40 to 120°F dew point	—	4°F/sec	±1.5°F	-40 to 120°F
Process Analyzers, Inc.	Moisture electrolyzer	1 to 1000 ppm	—	2 min	±5%	—
Honeywell, Inc.	LiCl with a gold grid	5 to 95% RH	SO_2, acid vapors, Cl_2, NH_3, HCCH, CH_2OCH_2	—	±2%	40 to 120°F
Phys-Chemical Research Corporation	Chemically treated styrene copolymer	0 to 100% RH	Oil vapors, sulfur compounds, water droplets	30 sec (63% change in RH)	±3%	-60 to 200°F

[a] RH = relative humidity.
These data represent only a few random examples in a rather extensive field. The specifications were taken from the manufacturers' product bulletins. It does not in any way constitute a product endorsement by the author or the U.S. Atomic Energy Commission.

193

Summary

The methods presented in Chapters 4 and 5 and much of Chapter 6 are briefly outlined here in order to compare and contrast their most important features. A brief scan of Table XXXIV will allow the experimenter to discard those systems that do not apply and to concentrate on those that are more suitable to his particular needs. This table is very general and should only be used as a rough guide.

Table XXXIV.   Characteristics of methods of

Method	Concentration range	Volume of test mixture produced	Average and best accuracy ($\pm\%$)	Operating pressure (atm)
Static systems				
Single vessel	10 ppm to 5%	10% of vessel volume	3 to 5, 1	≤1
Multiple vessels in series	10 ppm to 5%	Vessel volume[a]	5 to 10, 3	≤1
Nonrigid chambers	10 ppm to 5%	1 to 1000 liters	3, 1	1
Metering and compression	Low ppm to 50%	0.5 liter to 200 ft^3	3 to 5, 2	1 to 150
Manometric	100 ppm to 50%	0.5 liter to 200 ft^3	5 to 10, 1	1 to 150
Gravimetric	Low ppm to 50%	1 liter to 200 ft^3	0.1, 0.002	1 to 150
Partial evacuation	Low ppm to 50%	100 ml to 2 liters	1 to 5, 1	0.001 to 1
Dynamic systems				
Gas-stream mixing				
Single dilution	100 ppm to 50%	>200 ft^3	1 to 3, 1	≥1
Double dilution	Low ppb to 1%	>200 ft^3	5 to 10, 2 to 3	≥1
Motor-driven syringe				
Single	1 ppm to 0.1%	5 to 1000 liters	2 to 5, 1	≥1
Double	1 ppm to 0.5%	5 to 1000 liters	2 to 5, 1	≥1
Reciprocal	1 ppm to 2%	Very large	2 to 5, 1	≥1
Gravity feed	100 ppm to 5%	Large	5, 3	≥1
Pulse diluter	0.1 ppb to 0.1%	Very large	3 to 5, 1	≥1
Pumps	1 ppm to 5%	Very large	5, 1	≥1
Diffusion	0.1 to 500 ppm	Very large	2 to 6, 1	~1
Permeation	50 ppb to 200 ppm	Large	1 to 3, 0.5	~1
Evaporation	50 ppm to 10%	Large	3 to 15, 2	≥1
Electrolysis	Low ppm to 1%	Limited by solution, volume, and concentration	2 to 5, 1	~1
Chemical reaction	Low ppm to 1%	Limited by amount of reactants available	3 to 10, 1 to 3	~1

[a]Three vessels in series.
[b]"No" if downstream dilution is not available.
[c]Best for gases only.
[d]Best for liquids only.
[e]Longer if the temperature is altered.

producing controlled test atmospheres.

Degree of adsorption losses	Relative cost	Average time required to change concentrations	Relative complexity of the apparatus	Flushing required between concentration changes?	Dilution occur when part of test mixture removed?	Can evaporate liquids and combine vapors with diluent gas?	Can be used to make reactive gas mixtures?
Medium	Low	<10 min	Low	Yes	Yes	Yes	No
Medium	Low	<20 min	Low	Yes	Yes.	Yes	No
High	Very low	<10 min	Low	Yes	No	Not always	No
Medium	Medium	<1 min with dynamic dilution	Medium	Yes[b]	No	No[c]	Usually
Medium	High	<1 min with dynamic dilution	Medium	Yes[b]	No	No[c]	Usually
Medium	Medium to high	<1 min with dynamic dilution	Low	Yes[b]	No	Usually	Usually
Low to medium	Medium	<5 min	Low	No	No	Yes	Not always
Low	Low to medium	Seconds	Low	No	No	No[c]	Yes
Low	Medium	Several seconds	Low to medium	No	No	No[c]	Usually
Low	Medium to high	<1 min	Medium to high	No	No	Yes	Usually
Low	Medium to high	<1 min	Medium to high	No	No	Yes	Usually
Low	High	<1 min	Medium to high	No	No	Yes[d]	No
Low	Low	Several minutes	Low	No	No	Yes[d]	No
Low to medium	High	Hours	High	No	No	No	Yes
Low	Medium to high	<5 min	Medium	No	No	Yes	No
Low	Medium	Several minutes[e]	Low to medium	No	No	Yes[d]	No
Low	Low to medium	Several minutes[e]	Low to medium	No	No	Not always	Not always
Low	Low to medium	<5 min	Low	No	No	Yes[d]	No
Low	Medium	Several minutes	Medium	No	No	Not always	Yes
Low to medium	Medium	Several minutes	Medium	No	No	No	Yes

APPENDIX A:

CONVERSION FACTORS

LENGTH

cm	m	mm	in.	ft
1	0.01000	10.00	0.3937	0.03281
100.0	1	1000	39.37	3.281
1.1000	0.001000	1	0.03937	0.003281
2.540	0.02540	25.40	1	0.08333
30.48	0.3048	304.8	12.00	1

MASS

g	kg	lb	oz
1	0.001000	0.002205	0.03527
1000	1	2.205	35.27
543.6	0.5436	1	16.00
28.35	0.02835	0.06250	1

DENSITY

g/cm^3	$g/liter$	$lb/in.^3$	lb/ft^3
1	1,000	0.03613	62.43
0.001000	1	3.613×10^{-5}	0.06243
27.68	27,680	1	1,728
0.01602	16.02	5.787×10^{-4}	1

VOLUME

cm^3	$liter$	$in.^3$	ft^3	gal
1	0.001000	0.06103	3.531×10^{-5}	2.64×10^{-4}
1,000	1	61.03	0.03531	0.2642
16.39	0.01639	1	0.03579	0.02433
28,320	28.32	1,728	1	7.481
3,785	3.785	231.0	0.1337	1

PRESSURE

| kg/cm² | psi | atm | Height of Hg at 0°C | | Height of H_2O at 15°C | | psf | dynes/cm³ |
			mm	in.	mm	in.		
1	14.22	0.9678	735.5	28.90	10,010	394.1	2,048	9.807×10^5
0.07031	1	0.06804	51.71	2.036	703.7	27.70	144.0	6.895×10^4
1.033	14.70	1	760.0	29.92	10,340	407.1	2,116	1.013×10^6
0.001360	0.01934	0.001316	1	0.03937	13.61	0.5357	2.785	1,333
0.03453	0.4912	0.03342	25.40	1	345.6	13.61	70.73	3.386×10^4
9.991×10^{-5}	0.001421	9.670×10^{-5}	0.07349	0.002893	1	0.03937	0.2046	97.93
0.002538	0.03610	0.002456	1.867	0.07349	25.40	1	5.198	2,489
4.882×10^{-4}	0.006946	4.725×10^{-4}	0.3591	0.01414	4.887	0.1924	1	478.8
1.020×10^{-6}	1.450×10^{-5}	9.869×10^{-7}	7.501×10^{-4}	2.953×10^{-5}	0.01020	4.015×10^{-4}	0.002089	1

APPENDIX B:

ATOMIC WEIGHTS AND NUMBERS[a]

Name	Symbol	Atomic number	Atomic weight	Name	Symbol	Atomic number	Atomic weight
Actinium	Ac	89	—	Mercury	Hg	80	200.59
Aluminum	Al	13	26.9815	Molybdenum	Mo	42	95.94
Americium	Am	95	—	Neodymium	Nd	60	144.24
Antimony	Sb	51	121.75	Neon	Ne	10	20.183
Argon	Ar	18	39.948	Neptunium	Np	93	—
Arsenic	As	33	74.9216	Nickel	Ni	28	58.71
Astatine	At	85	—	Niobium	Nb	41	92.906
Barium	Ba	56	137.34	Nitrogen	N	7	14.0067
Berkelium	Bk	97	—	Nobelium	No	102	—
Beryllium	Be	4	9.0122	Osmium	Os	75	190.2
Bismuth	Bi	83	208.980	Oxygen	O	8	15.9994
Boron	B	5	10.811	Palladium	Pd	46	106.4
Bromine	Br	35	79.904	Phosphorus	P	15	30.9738
Cadmium	Cd	48	112.40	Platinum	Pt	78	195.09
Caesium	Cs	55	132.905	Plutonium	Pu	94	—
Calcium	Ca	20	40.08	Polonium	Po	84	—
Californium	Cf	98	—	Potassium	K	19	39.102
Carbon	C	6	12.01115	Praseodym	Pr	59	140.907
Cerium	Ce	58	140.12	Promethium	Pm	61	—
Chlorine	Cl	17	35.453	Protactinium	Pa	91	—
Chromium	Cr	24	51.996	Radium	Ra	88	—
Cobalt	Co	27	58.9332	Radon	Rn	86	—
Copper	Cu	29	63.546	Rhenium	Re	75	186.2
Curium	Cm	96	—	Rhodium	Rh	45	102.905
Dysprosium	Dy	66	162.50	Rubidium	Rb	37	84.57

Einsteinium	Es	99	—	Ruthenium	Ru	44	101.07
Erbium	Er	68	167.26	Samarium	Sm	62	150.35
Europium	Eu	63	151.96	Scandium	Sc	21	44.956
Fermium	Fm	100	—	Selenium	Se	34	78.96
Fluorine	F	9	18.9984	Silicon	Si	14	28.086
Francium	Fr	87	—	Silver	Ag	47	107.868
Gadolinium	Gd	64	157.25	Sodium	Na	11	22.9898
Gallium	Ga	31	69.72	Strontium	Sr	38	87.62
Germanium	Ge	32	72.59	Sulfur	S	16	32.064
Gold	Au	79	196.967	Tantalum	Ta	73	180.948
Hafnium	Hf	72	178.49	Technetium	Tc	43	—
Helium	He	2	4.0026	Tellurium	Te	52	127.60
Holmium	Ho	67	164.930	Terbium	Tb	65	158.924
Hydrogen	H	1	1.00797	Thallium	Tl	81	204.37
Indium	In	49	114.82	Thorium	Th	90	232.038
Iodine	I	53	126.9044	Thulium	Tm	59	168.934
Iridium	Ir	77	192.2	Tin	Sn	50	118.69
Iron	Fe	26	55.847	Titanium	Ti	22	47.90
Krypton	Kr	36	83.80	Tungsten	W	74	183.85
Lanthanum	La	57	138.91	Uranium	U	92	238.03
Lawrencium	Lr	103	—	Vanadium	V	23	50.942
Lead	Pb	82	207.19	Xenon	Xe	54	131.30
Lithium	Li	3	6.939	Ytterbium	Yb	70	173.04
Lutetium	Lu	71	174.97	Yttrium	Y.	39	88.905
Magnesium	Mg	12	24.312	Zinc	Zn	30	65.37
Manganese	Mn	25	54.9380	Zirconium	Zr	40	91.22
Mendelevium	Md	101	—				

aData taken from Reference 397. All atomic weights are based on $C^{12} = 12$. The atomic weights in this table apply to elements as they exist in nature, without artificial alteration of their isotopic composition, as well as to natural mixtures that do not include isotopes of radiogenic origin.

APPENDIX C:

VALUES OF THE MOLAR GAS CONSTANT

Value	Unit
0.082054	(liter)(atm)/(g-mole)(°K)
82.057	(ml)(atm)/(g-mole)(°K)
62.361	(liter)(mm Hg)/(g-mole)(°K)
1.9872	(cal)/(g-mole)(°K)
8.3130	(J)/(g-mole)(°K)
849.9	(liter)(kg/m^2)/(g-mole)(°K)
1.986	(BTU)/(lb-mole)(°R)
0.7302	(ft^3)(atm)/(lb-mole)(°R)
10.731	(ft^3)(lb)/(in.^{2})(lb-mole)(°R)
555.0	(ft^3)(mm Hg)/(lb-mole)(°R)
21.85	(ft^3)(in. Hg)/(lb-mole)(°R)

APPENDIX D:

DENSITY OF DRY AIR[a]

Temperature (°C)	Density (in g/liter) at:			
	720 mm Hg	740 mm Hg	760 mm Hg	780 mm Hg
0	1.2248	1.2589	1.2929	1.3269
5	1.2029	1.2363	1.2697	1.3031
10	1.1815	1.2144	1.2472	1.2800
15	1.1611	1.1933	1.2256	1.2578
20	1.1413	1.1730	1.2047	1.2364
25	1.1221	1.1533	1.1845	1.2157
30	1.1036	1.1342	1.1649	1.1955
35	1.0857	1.1158	1.1460	1.1762
40	1.0683	1.0980	1.1277	1.1574

[a]The average molecular weight of air is 28.96 g/mole.

APPENDIX E:

DENSITIES OF COMMON GASES AND THEIR DEVIATION FROM THE PERFECT GAS LAW

Compound	Formula	Molecular weight	Boiling point (°C)	Vapor density at 0°C and 760 mm Hg		Density ratios at 0°C and 760 mm Hg	
				Experimental ρ_A	Calculated ρ_I	ρ_A/ρ_I	ρ_A/ρ_{air}
Acetylene	HCCH	26.04	-84	1.1708	1.1627	1.0079	0.9056
Air	—	28.96	-183	1.2929	1.2920	1.0007	1.0000
Allene	CH_2CCH_2	40.07	-34	1.787	1.7887	0.9994	1.382
Ammonia	NH_3	17.03	-33	0.7710	0.7598	1.015	0.5963
Argon	Ar	39.94	-185	1.784	1.782	1.001	1.380
Arsine	A_sH_3	77.94	-62	3.485	3.477	1.002	2.695
Boron trichloride	BCl_3	117.19	-12.5	5.3	5.228	1.02	4.1
Boron trifluoride	BF_3	67.82	-100	3.06	3.025	1.010	2.37
Bromotrifluoro-ethylene	CF_2CFBr	160.93	-2	7.2	7.180	1.011	56
Bromotrifluoro-methane	$CBrF_3$	148.93	-58	6.83	6.645	1.029	5.28
1,3-Butadiene	$CH_2CHCHCH_2$	54.09	-4	2.476	2.413	1.026	1.915
n-Butane	$CH_3CH_2CH_2CH_3$	58.12	-0.5	2.696	2.593	1.040	2.085
1-Butene	$CH_3CH_2CHCH_2$	56.11	-6	2.583	2.503	1.032	1.998

Name	Formula						
2-Butene	$CH_3CHCHCH_3$	56.11	-2	2.582	2.503	1.032	1.997
1-Butyne	CH_3CH_2CCH	54.09	8	2.542	2.413	1.053	1.966
Carbon dioxide	CO_2	44.01	-79	1.977	1.963	1.007	1.529
Carbon monoxide	CO	28.01	-192	1.251	1.250	1.001	0.9676
Carbonyl sulfide	COS	60.08	-52	2.72	2.680	1.02	2.10
Chlorine	Cl_2	70.91	-34	3.214	3.164	1.016	2.486
Chlorine dioxide	ClO_2	67.46	10	3.21	3.010	1.03	2.48
Chlorine trifluoride	ClF_3	92.46	11.8	4.06	4.125	0.983	3.14
Chlorodefluoro-methane	$CHClF_2$	86.48	-41	4.01	3.858	1.04	3.10
Chloropentafluoro-ethane	CF_3CF_2Cl	154.48	-39	7.17	6.892	1.04	5.54
Chlorotrifluoro-ethylene	CH_2CFCl	116.48	-28	5.3	5.197	1.02	4.1
Chlorotrifluoro-methane	CF_3Cl	104.47	-81	4.86	4.661	1.03	3.71
Cyanogen	$NCCN$	52.04	-21.2	2.335	2.322	1.006	1.806
Cyclopropane	$-(CH_2)_3-$	92.08	-33	1.87	1.877	0.995	1.45
Deuterium	D_2	4.032	-250	0.1800	0.1799	1.0006	0.1392
Diborane	B_2H_6	27.67	-93	1.2	1.234	0.97	0.93
Dibromodifluoro-methane	CBr_2F_2	209.84	24.5	—	9.362	—	7.241
Dichlorodifluoro-methane	CF_2Cl_2	120.93	-30	5.50	5.395	1.019	4.25

Compound	Formula	Molecular weight	Boiling point (°C)	Vapor density at 0°C and 760 mm Hg		Density ratios at 0°C and 760 mm Hg	
				Experimental ρ_A	Calculated ρ_I	ρ_A/ρ_I	ρ_A/ρ_{air}
Dichlorofluoromethane	$CHFCl_2$	102.93	8.9	4.70	4.592	1.024	3.63
1,2-Dichlorotetrafluoroethane	CF_2ClCF_2Cl	170.93	3.6	7.75	7.626	1.016	5.99
1,1-Difluoro-1-chloroethane	CH_3CF_2Cl	100.50	-9	—	4.484	—	3.468
1,1-Difluoroethane	CH_3CHF_2	66.05	-25	3.2	2.947	1.09	2.5
1,1-Difluoroethylene	CH_2CF_2	64.04	-83	2.9	2.857	1.02	2.2
Dimethylamine	$(CH_3)_2NH$	45.08	6.9	2.00	2.011	0.995	1.55
Dimethyl ether	$(CH_3)_2O$	46.07	-25	2.091	2.055	1.018	1.617
2,2-Dimethylpropane	$(CH_3)_4C$	72.15	9.5	3.390	3.219	1.053	2.622
Ethane	CH_3CH_3	30.07	-89	1.356	1.342	1.010	1.049
Ethyl chloride	CH_3CH_2Cl	64.52	12.4	2.87	2.879	1.00	2.22
Ethylene	CH_2CH_2	28.05	-104	1.262	1.251	1.009	0.9765
Ethylene oxide	$-CH_2OCH_2-$	44.05	10.7	1.92	1.963	0.975	1.49
Fluorine	F_2	38.00	-188	1.696	1.695	1.001	1.312
Flyoroethane	CH_3CH_2F	48.06	-38	2.16	2.144	1.009	1.67

Fluoroform	CHF$_3$	70.02	-84	3.2	3.124	1.02	2.5
Germane	GeH$_4$	76.63	-90	3.43	3.419	1.003	2.65
Helium	He	4.003	-269	0.1785	0.1786	0.9994	0.1381
Hexafluoroacetone	(CF$_3$)$_2$CO	166.07	-28	—	7.409	—	5.731
Hexafluoroethane	CF$_3$CF$_3$	138.05	-78	6.44	6.159	1.045	4.98
Hydrogen	H$_2$	2.016	-253	0.08986	0.08994	0.9991	0.06950
Hydrogen bromide	HBr	80.92	-66	3.50	3.610	0.970	2.71
Hydrogen chloride	HCl	36.47	-85	1.639	1.627	1.007	1.268
Hydrogen fluoride	HF	20.01	19.5	1.06	0.8927	1.19	0.820
Hydrogen iodide	HI	127.92	-35.5	5.72	5.707	1.002	4.42
Hydrogen selenide	H$_2$Se	80.98	-41	—	3.613	—	2.794
Hydrogen sulfide	H$_2$S	34.08	-60	1.538	1.520	1.012	1.190
Isobutane	(CH$_3$)$_3$CH	58.12	-12	2.60	2.593	1.003	2.01
Isobutene	(CH$_3$)$_2$CCH$_2$	56.11	-7	2.582	2.503	1.032	1.997
Krypton	Kr	83.80	-153	3.749	3.739	1.003	2.900
Methane	CH$_4$	16.04	-162	0.7168	0.7156	1.002	0.5544
Methyl acetylene	CH$_3$CCH	40.07	-23	1.826	1.788	1.021	1.412
Methyl bromide	CH$_3$Br	94.95	3.5	4.265	4.236	1.007	3.299
Methyl chloride	CH$_3$Cl	50.49	-24	2.28	2.253	1.013	1.76
Methyl fluoride	CH$_3$F	34.03	-78	1.545	1.518	1.018	1.195
Methyl mercaptan	CH$_3$SH	48.10	6	2.15	2.146	1.00	1.66

Compound	Formula	Molecular weight	Boiling point (°C)	Vapor density at 0°C and 760 mm Hg		Density ratios at 0°C and 760 mm Hg	
				Experimental ρ_A	Calculated ρ_I	ρ_A/ρ_I	ρ_A/ρ_{air}
Monomethylamine	CH_3NH_2	31.06	-6.5	1.38	1.386	0.995	1.07
Neon	Ne	20.18	-246	0.9002	0.9005	0.9997	0.6963
Nickel carbonyl	$Ni(CO)_4$	170.75	43	—	7.618	—	5.892
Nitric oxide	NO	30.01	-152	1.341	1.339	1.001	1.037
Nitrogen	N_2	28.016	-196	1.2506	1.2499	1.0006	0.9673
Nitrogen dioxide	NO_2	46.01	21.3	3.9[a]	2.053	1.9	—
Nitrogen trioxide	N_2O_3	76.02	3.5	—	3.392	—	2.450
Nitrogen trifluoride	NF_3	71.01	-129	—	3.168	—	2.259
Nitrosyl chloride	NOCl	65.47	-6	2.99	2.921	1.024	2.31
Nitrous oxide	N_2O	44.02	-89.5	1.978	1.964	1.007	1.530
Oxygen	O_2	32.00	-183	1.429	1.428	1.001	1.105
Oxygen difluoride	OF_2	54.00	-145	—	2.409	—	1.863
Ozone	O_3	48.00	-182	2.144	2.141	1.001	1.658
Perfluoro-2-butene	$CF_3CFCFCF_3$	200.04	1.2	—	8.925	—	6.903
Perfluorocyclobutane	$-(CF_2)_4-$	200.04	-6	9.41	8.925	1.055	7.28
Perfluoropropane	$CF_3CF_2CF_3$	188.03	-37	8.56	8.389	1.020	6.62
Phosgene	Cl_2CO	98.93	8	4.4	4.414	1.00	3.4
Phosphene	PH_5	34.00	-88	1.482	1.517	0.977	1.146

Phosphorous pentafluoride	PF_5	125.98	-85	5.805	5.620	1.033	4.490
Propane	$CH_3CH_2CH_3$	44.10	-42	2.015	1.967	1.024	1.559
Propylene	CH_3CHCH_2	42.08	-48	1.937	1.877	1.032	1.498
Selenium hexafluoride	SeF_6	192.96	-34	—	8.609	—	6.659
Silane	SiH_4	32.12	-112	1.44	1.433	1.007	1.11
Silicon tetrafluoride	SiF_4	104.09	-65	4.67	4.644	1.006	3.61
Stibine	SbH_3	124.77	-17[b]	5.61	5.567	1.007	4.34
Sulfur hexafluoride	SF_6	146.07	-64	6.61	6.517	1.013	5.11
Sulfur dioxide	SO_2	64.07	-10	2.927	2.858	1.024	2.264
Sulfur tetrafluoride	SF_4	108.07	-40	—	4.821	—	3.729
Sulfuryl fluoride	SO_2F_2	102.07	-55	4.55	4.554	1.00	3.52
Tetrafluoromethane	CF_4	88.01	-128	4.05	3.927	1.031	3.13
Trimethylamine	$(CH_3)_3N$	59.11	3.5	2.7	2.637	1.02	2.1
Vinyl bromide	CH_2CHBr	106.96	16	4.9	4.772	1.03	3.8
Vinyl chloride	CH_2CHCl	62.50	-14	2.78	2.788	0.996	2.15
Vinyl fluoride	CH_2CHF	46.04	-51	2.1	2.054	1.02	1.6
Vinyl methyl ether	CH_2CHOCH_3	58.08	7	2.6	2.591	1.00	2.0
Xenon	Xe	131.30	-108	5.897	5.858	1.007	4.561

[a] At 0°C, nitrogen dioxide exists almost entirely as N_2O_4.
[b] At 751 mm Hg.

APPENDIX F:

DIFFUSION COEFFICIENTS AT 25°C AND 760 mm Hg IN AIR[a]

Compound	Formula	Diffusion coefficient (cm^2/sec)
Acetic acid	CH_3COOH	0.1235
Acetone	$(CH_3)_2CO$	0.1049
Acrylonitrile	CH_2CHCN	0.1059
Allyl alcohol	CH_2CHCH_2OH	0.1021
Allyl chloride	CH_2CHCH_2Cl	0.0975
Amyl acetate	$CH_3COO(CH_2)_4CH_3$	0.0610
Amyl alcohol	$CH_3(CH_2)_3CH_2OH$	0.0716
sec-Amyl alcohol	$CH_3CH_2CH_2CH(OH)CH_3$	0.0728
Amyl butyrate	$CH_3(CH_2)_2COO(CH_2)_4CH_3$	0.0486
Amyl-isobutyrate	$(CH_3)_2CHCOO(CH_2)_4CH_3$	0.0496
Amyl formate	$HCOO(CH_2)_4CH_3$	0.0663
iso-Amyl formate	$HCOO(CH_2)_2CH(CH_3)_2$	0.0675
n-Amyl propionate	$CH_3CH_2COO(CH_2)_4CH_3$	0.0559
Aniline	$C_6H_5NH_2$	0.0735
Benzene	C_6H_6	0.0932
Benzonitrile	C_6H_5CN	0.0710
Benzyl acetate	$CH_3COOCH_2C_6H_5$	0.0600
Benzyl alcohol	$C_6H_5CH_2OH$	0.0712
Benzyl chloride	$C_6H_5CH_2Cl$	0.0713
Bromine	Br_2	0.1064
Bromochloromethane	CH_2ClBr	0.9953
Bromoform	$CHBr_3$	0.0767
Butyl acetate	$CH_3COO(CH_2)_3CH_3$	0.0672
ios-Butyl acetate	$CH_3COOCH_2CH(CH_3)_2$	0.0690
iso-Butyl alcohol	$(CH_3)_2CHCH_2OH$	0.0880
Butyl alcohol	$CH_3(CH_2)_2CH_2OH$	0.0861
sec-Butyl alcohol	$CH_3CH_2CH(OH)CH_3$	0.0891
tert-Butyl alcohol	$(CH_3)_3COH$	0.0873
Butylamine	$CH_3(CH_2)_3NH_2$	0.0872

Compound	Formula	Diffusion coefficient (cm^2/sec)
iso-Butyl amine	$(CH_3)_2CHCH_2NH_2$	0.0900
iso-Butyl-iso-butyrate	$(CH_3)_2CHCOOCH_2CH(CH_3)_2$	0.0551
Butyl ether	$[CH_3(CH_2)_3]_2O$	0.0536
iso-Butyl formate	$HCOOCH_2CH(CH_3)_2$	0.0784
iso-Butyl butyrate	$CH_3(CH_2)_2COOCH_2CH(CH_3)_2$	0.0559
iso-Butyl propionate	$CH_3CH_2COOCH_2CH(CH_3)_2$	0.0611
Butyl propionate	$CH_3CH_2COO(CH_2)_3CH_3$	0.0608
iso-Butyl valerate	$CH_3(CH_2)_3COOCH_2CH(CH_3)_2$	0.0494
iso-Butyric acid	$(CH_3)_2CHCOOH$	0.0785
Butyric acid	$CH_3(CH_2)_2COOH$	0.0775
iso-Caproic acid	$(CH_3)_2CH(CH_2)_2COOH$	0.0596
Caproic acid	$CH_3(CH_2)_4COOH$	0.0602
Carbon disulfide	CS_2	0.1045
Carbon tetrachloride	CCl_4	0.0828
Chlorobenzene	C_6H_5Cl	0.0747
Chloroform	$CHCl_3$	0.0888
Chloropicrin	CCl_3NO_2	0.0811
m-Chlorotoluene	$CH_3C_6H_4Cl$	0.0645
o-Chlorotoluene	$CH_3C_6H_4Cl$	0.0688
p-Chlorotoluene	$CH_3C_6H_4Cl$	0.0621
p-Cymene	$CH_3C_6H_4CH(CH_3)_2$	0.0630
Diacetone alcohol	$(CH_3)_2C(OH)CH_2COCH_3$	0.0647
1,2-Dibromo-3-chloropropane	$CH_2BrCHBrCH_2Cl$	0.0686
1,2-Dibromoethane	CH_2BrCH_2Br	0.0826
Dibutyl phthalate	$C_6H_4[COO(CH_2)_3CH_3]_2$	0.0421
1,1-Dichloroethane	$CHCl_2CH_3$	0.0919
1,2-Dichloroethane	CH_2ClCH_2Cl	0.0907
sym-Dichloroethyl ether	$(ClCH_2CH_2)_2O$	0.0694
Dichloromethane	CH_2Cl_2	0.1037
1,2-Dichloropropane	$CH_3CHClCH_2Cl$	0.0794
Diethyl amine	$(C_2H_5)_2NH$	0.0993

Compound	Formula	Diffusion coefficient (cm^2/sec)
Diethylene glycol	$[CH_2OHCH_2]_2O$	0.0730
Diethylene glycol monoethyl ether	$C_2H_5OCH_2CH_2OCH_2CH_2OH$	0.0610
Di-2-ethyl hexyl phosphate	$[CH_3(CH_2)_3CH(C_2H_5)CH_2O]_2PO_2$	0.0394
Dimethyl formamide	$HCON(CH_3)_2$	0.0973
Di-iso-octyl phthalate	$C_6H_4[COO(CH_2)_5CH(CH_3)_2]$	0.0337
Dioxane	$-O(CH_2)_2O(CH_2)_2-$	0.0922
Diethyl phthalate	$C_6H_4(COOC_2H_5)_2$	0.0497
Ethyl acetate	$CH_3COOC_2H_5$	0.0861
Ethyl alcohol	C_2H_5OH	0.1181
Ethylbenzene	$C_6H_5CH_2CH_3$	0.0755
Ethyl bromide	CH_3CH_2Br	0.0989
2-Ethyl-1-butanol	$(C_2H_5)_2CHCH_2OH$	0.0656
Ethyl-iso-butyrate	$(CH_3)_2CHCOOC_2H_5$	0.0675
Ethyl butyrate	$CH_3(CH_2)_2COOC_2H_5$	0.0669
Ethylene chlorohydrin	CH_2ClCH_2OH	0.0964
Ethyl cyanoacetate	$CHCH_2COOC_2H_5$	0.0710
Ethyl ether	$(C_2H_5)_2O$	0.0918
Ethylene diamine	$H_2NCH_2CH_2NH_2$	0.1009
Ethylene glycol	CH_2OHCH_2OH	0.1005
Ethylene glycol monoethyl ether	$CH_2OHCH_2OC_2H_5$	0.0788
Ethylene glycol monomethyl ether	$CH_2OHCH_2OCH_3$	0.0884
Ethyl formate	$HCOOC_2H_5$	0.0976
Ethyl propionate	$CH_3CH_2COOC_2H_5$	0.0766
Ethyl valerate	$CH_3(CH_2)_3COOC_2H_5$	0.0603
Formic acid	$HCOOH$	0.1530
n-Heptyl alcohol	$CH_3(CH_2)_5CH_2OH$	0.0554
n-Hexane	$CH_3(CH_2)_4CH_3$	0.0732
Hexyl alcohol	$CH_3(CH_2)_4CH_2OH$	0.0621
Mercury	Hg	0.1423

Compound	Formula	Diffusion coefficient (cm^2/sec)
Mesitylene	$C_6H_3(CH_3)_3$	0.0663
Mesityl oxide	$(CH_3)_2CCHCOCH_3$	0.0760
Methyl acetate	CH_3COOCH_3	0.0978
Methyl alcohol	CH_3OH	0.1520
Methyl-iso-butyrate	$(CH_3)_2CHCOOCH_3$	0.0748
Methyl butyrate	$CH_3(CH_2)_2COOCH_3$	0.0745
Methyl n-caproate	$CH_3(CH_2)_4COOCH_3$	0.0610
Methyl ethyl ketone	$CH_3COC_2H_5$	0.0903
Methyl fomate	$HCOOCH_3$	0.1090
Methyl propionate	$CH_3CH_2COOCH_3$	0.0862
Methyl propyl ketone	$CH_3COC_3H_7$	0.0793
Methyl valerate	$CH_3(CH)_3COOCH_3$	0.0665
Nitrobenzene	$C_6H_5NO_2$	0.0721
Octane	$CH_3(CH_2)_6CH_3$	0.0616
Octyl alcohol	$CH_3(CH_2)_7OH$	0.0506
Pentachloroethane	CCl_3CCl_2H	0.0673
Pentane	$CH_3(CH_2)_3CH_3$	0.0842
Propionic acid	C_2H_5COOH	0.0952
iso-Propyl acetate	$CH_3COOCH(CH_3)_2$	0.0770
Propyl acetate	$CH_3COOCH_2CH_2CH_3$	0.0768
iso-Propyl alcohol	$(CH_3)_2CHOH$	0.1013
Propyl alcohol	$CH_3CH_2CH_2OH$	0.0993
iso-Propylbenzene	$C_6H_5CH(CH_3)_2$	0.0677
Propylbenzene	$C_6H_5(CH_2)_2CH_3$	0.0669
iso-Propyl bromide	$(CH_3)_2CHBr$	0.0914
Propyl bromide	$CH_3CH_2CH_2Br$	0.0875
iso-Propyl-iso-butyrate	$(CH_3)_2CHCOOCH(CH_3)_2$	0.0638
Propyl-iso-butyrate	$(CH_3)_2CHCOOC_3H_7$	0.0622
Propyl butyrate	$CH_3(CH_2)_2COOC_3H_7$	0.0610
iso-Propyl ether	$[(CH_3)_2CH]_2O$	0.0683
Propylene glycol	$CH_3CHOHCH_2OH$	0.0879
Propyl formate	$HCOOC_3H_7$	0.0831

Compound	Formula	Diffusion coefficient (cm^2/sec)
iso-Propyl iodide	$(CH_3)_2CHI$	0.0878
Propyl iodide	$CH_3CH_2CH_2I$	0.0868
Propyl valerate	$CH_3(CH_2)_3COOC_3H_7$	0.0556
Pseudocumene	$C_6H_3(CH_3)_3$	0.0642
Styrene	$C_6H_5CHCH_2$	0.0701
1,1,2,2-Tetrachlorethane	CCl_2HCCl_2H	0.0722
Tetrachloroethylene	Cl_2CCCl_2	0.0797
Tetraethyl pyrophosphate	$[(C_2H_5)_2PO_3]_2O$	0.0475
Toluene	$C_6H_5CH_3$	0.0849
Toluene di-iso-cyanate	$CH_3C_6H_6(NCO)_2$	0.0583
Tributyl phosphate	$[CH_3(CH_2)_3]_3PO_4$	0.0432
1,1,1-Trichlorethane	CCl_3CH_3	0.0794
1,1,2-Trichlorethane	CCl_2HCClH_2	0.0792
Trichlorethylene	$ClHCCCl_2$	0.0875
Triethyl amine	$(C_2H_5)_3N$	0.0754
Triethylene glycol	$CH_2OHCH_2OCH_2CH_2OCH_2CH_2OH$	0.0590
Triethyl phosphate	$(C_2H_5)_3PO_4$	0.0552
iso-Valeric acid	$(CH_3)_2CHCH_2COOH$	0.0653
m-Xylene	$C_6H_4(CH_3)_2$	0.0670
o-Xylene	$C_6H_4(CH_3)_2$	0.0727
p-Xylene	$C_6H_4(CH_3)_2$	0.0670

[a]Data taken from Reference 267.

APPENDIX G:
CONSTANTS FOR VAPOR-PRESSURE CALCULATIONS[a]

Compound	Formula	Temperature range (°C)	Constants A	B	C
Acetaldehyde	CH_3CHO	-45 to 70	6.8109	992.0	230
Acetic acid	CH_3COOH	0 to 36	7.803	1651	225
Acetone	CH_3COCH_3	—	7.0245	1161	224
Acetonitrile	—	—	7.120	1314	230
Acrylonitrile	—	-20 to 140	7.039	1233	222.5
Ammonia	NH_3	-83 to 60	7.555	1003	247.9
Amylbenzene	$CH_3(CH_2)_4C_6H_5$	15 to 104	7.3517	1858.4	212.0
Aniline	$C_6H_5NH_2$	—	7.2418	1675.3	200
Benzene	C_6H_6	—	6.9056	1211.0	220.79
Benzonitrile	C_6H_5CN	—	6.7463	1436.7	181.0
Benzotrifluoride	$C_6H_5CF_3$	-20 to 180	7.0071	1331.3	220.58
Benzil alcohol	$C_6H_5CH_2OH$	20 to 113	7.8184	1950.3	194.4
Bromine	BR_2	—	6.8330	1133	228
Bromobenzene	C_6H_5Br	—	6.8834	1440	204
Bromocyclohexane	$C_6H_{11}Br$	0 to 68	7.3414	1778.8	235
p-Bromotoluene	$CH_3C_6H_4Br$	10 to 85	7.2284	1743.7	218
1,3-Butadiene	$CH_2CHCHCH_2$	-80 to 65	6.8594	935.5	239.5
n-Butane	$CH_3CH_2CH_2CH$	—	6.8303	945.9	240
iso-Butane	$(CH_3)_3CH$	—	6.7481	882.8	240
1-Butene	$CH_2CHCH_2CH_3$	—	6.8429	926.1	240
tert-Butyl alcohol	$(CH_3)_3COH$	—	8.1360	1582.4	218.9
n-Butylchloride	$CH_3(CH_2)_3Cl$	—	6.7520	1125.8	212
Carbon disulfide	CS_2	-10 to 160	6.8514	1122.5	236.5
Carbon tetrachloride	CCl_4	—	6.9339	1242.4	230
Chlorine	Cl_2	—	6.8677	821.1	240
Chlorobenzene	C_6H_5Cl	0 to 42	7.1069	1500	224
o-Chloroethylbenzene	$CH_3CH_2C_6H_4Cl$	—	6.9817	1556	201
Chloroform	$CHCl_3$	-30 to 150	6.90328	1163.0	227.4
o-Chlorophenol	ClC_6H_4OH	15 to 80	7.2420	1668	210
o-Chlorotoluene	$CH_3C_6H_4Cl$	0 to 65	7.3680	1735.8	230
p-Cresol	$CH_3C_6H_4OH$	—	7.0059	1493	160
Cyclohexane	C_6H	-50 to 200	6.845	1203.5	222.9
Cyclohexene	$-(CH)_2(CH_2)_4-$	—	6.8862	1230	224
Cyclopentane	$-(CH_2)_5-$	—	6.8868	1124.2	231.4
Cyclopentene	$-(CH)_2(CH_2)_3-$	—	6.9207	1121.8	233.4
Decane	$CH_3(CH_2)_8CH_3$	10 to 80	7.3151	1705.6	212.6
1,3-Dibromopropane	$(CH_2Br)_2CH_2$	0 to 71	7.54984	1890.56	240

Compound	Formula	Temperature range (°C)	Constants A	B	C
o-Dichlorobenzene	ClC_6H_4Cl	—	6.9240	1538.3	200
Diethylamine	$(C_2H_5)_2NH$	-30 to 100	6.8319	1057.2	212.0
o-Diethylbenzene	$(C_2H_5)_2C_6H_4$	—	6.9902	1577.9	200.6
Diethyl ether	$(C_2H_5)_2O$	—	6.7857	994.2	220.0
Diethyl ketone	$(C_2G_5)_2CO$	—	6.8579	1216.3	204
Diethyl sulfide	$(C_2H_5)_2S$	0 to 150	6.9284	1257.8	218.7
Dimethyl ether	$(CH_3)_2O$	—	6.7367	791.18	230.0
Dimethyl formamide	$(CH_3)_2NCHO$	15 to 60	7.3438	1624.7	216.2
Dipropyl sulfide	$(CH_3CH_2CH_2)_2S$	0 to 53	7.2831	1599	222.2
Ethane	CH_3CH_3	—	6.8027	656.4	256
Ethyl acetate	$CH_3CH_2COOCH_2CH_3$	-20 to 150	7.0981	1238.7	217
Ethyl alcohol	CH_3CH_2OH	—	8.0449	1554.3	222.7
Ethyl benzene	$C_6H_5C_2H_5$	—	6.9572	1424.3	213.2
Ethyl bromide	C_2H_5Br	-50 to 130	6.8929	1083.8	231.7
Ethyl chloride	C_2H_5Cl	-65 to 70	6.8027	949.6	230
Ethylene	C_2H_4	—	6.7476	585.0	255.0
Ethylene bromide	$(CH_2Br)_2$	—	7.0624	1469.7	220.1
Ethylene chloride	$(CH_2Cl)_2$	—	7.1843	1358.5	232.2
Ethylene oxide	$(CH_2)_2O$	-70 to 100	7.4078	1181.3	250.6
Ethyl formate	$HCOOCH_2CH_3$	-30 to 235	7.1170	1176.6	223.
Ethyl mercaptan	C_2H_5SH	-40 to 100	6.9521	1084.5	231.4
p-Ethyl toluene	$CH_3CH_2C_6H_5$	—	6.9980	1527.1	209
Fluorobenzene	C_6H_5F	-40 to 180	6.9367	1736.4	220.0
Formic acid	$HCOOH$	—	6.9446	1295.3	218
Furan	$-(CH_2)_2O(CH_2)_2-$	-35 to 90	6.9752	1060.9	227.7
Neptane	$CH_3(CH_2)_5CH_3$	—	6.9024	1268.1	216.9
1-Heptene	$CH_2CH(CH_2)_4CH_3$	—	6.9007	1257.5	219.2
Hexachloropropene	$Cl_2CCClCCl_3$	20 to 109	7.2664	1863.7	213
Hexane	$CH_3(CH_2)_4CH_3$	—	6.8778	1171.5	224.4
1-Hexene	$CH_2CH(CH_2)_3CH_3$	—	6.8657	1153.0	225.85
Hydrazene	$(NH_2)_2$	-10 to 39	8.2623	1881.6	238.0
Hydrogen cyanade	HCN	-40 to 70	7.2976	1206.8	247.5
Hydrogen fluoride	HF	-55 to 105	8.3804	1952.6	335.5
Iodine	I_2	—	7.2630	1697.9	204
Iodobenzene	C_6H_5I	—	6.8951	1562.87	201
Methyl acetate	CH_3COOCH_3	—	7.2021	1232.8	228
Methyl alcohol		-20 to 140	7.8786	1473.1	230
Methyl amine	CH_3NH_2	-45 to 50	6.9121	838.1	214.2
Methyl aniline	$C_6H_5NH_2$	—	7.2258	1728.2	202
Methylene chlorobromide	CH_2ClBr	-10 to 155	6.9278	1166.0	220

Compound	Formula	Temperature range (°C)	Constants A	B	C
Methyl ethyl ketone	$CH_3COCH_2CH_3$	—	6.9742	1209.6	216
Methyl formate	$HCOOCH_3$	—	7.1362	1111	229.2
Morpholine	$-O(CH_2)_2NH(CH_2)_2-$	0 to 44	7.71813	1745.8	235
Naphthalene	$C_{10}H_8$	—	6.8458	1606.5	187.2
Nonane	$CH_3(CH_2)_7CH_3$	-10 to 60	7.2643	1607.1	217.5
Octane	$CH_3(CH_2)_6CH_3$	-20 to 40	7.3720	1587.8	230.1
Ozone	O_3	—	6.7260	566.9	260
Pentane	$CH_3(CH_2)_3CH_3$	—	6.8522	1064.6	232
Phenol	C_6H_5OH	—	7.1362	1518.1	175
Phosgene	CCl_2O	-68 to 68	6.8430	941.3	230
Phosphine	PH_3	—	6.7010	643.7	256
Phosphorus pentachloride	PCl_5	—	9.4274	2422.2	208
Propadiene	CH_2CCH_2	-100 to 40	5.6457	441	194
Propane	$CH_3CH_2CH_3$	—	6.8297	813.2	248
Propionic acid	CH_3CH_2COOH	0 to 60	7.7156	1690	210
Propyl acetate	$CH_3COOCH_2CH_2CH_3$	0 to 170	7.0667	1304.1	210
Propyl alcohol	$CH_3CH_2CH_2OH$	—	7.9973	1569.7	209.5
iso-Propyl alcohol	$(CH_3)_2CHOH$	0 to 113	6.6604	813.0	132.9
Propyl benzene	$CH_3CH_2CH_2C_6H_5$	—	6.9514	1491.3	207.1
Propylene	CH_2CHCH_3	—	6.8196	785	247
1,2-Propylene oxide	CH_2OCHCH_3	-35 to 130	7.0649	1113.6	232
Selenium dioxide	SeO_2	—	6.5778	1879.8	179
Styrene	$C_6H_5CHCH_2$	—	6.9241	1420	206
Sulfur	S	—	6.6954	2285.4	155
Sulfur dioxide	SO_2	—	7.3278	1022.8	240
Tetrachloroethylene	Cl_2CCCl_2	—	7.0200	1415.5	221
Thiophene	$-(CH)_2S(CH)_2-$	-10 to 180	6.9593	1246	221
Toluene	$C_6H_5CH_3$	—	6.9546	1344.8	219.5
1,1,2-Tribromoethane	$CHBr_2CH_2Br$	20 to 90	7.337	1789	215
1,2,4-Trichlorobenzene	$C_6H_3Cl_3$	20 to 109	7.555	2064	230.1
1,1,2-Trichloroethane	$CHCl_2CH_2Cl$	—	6.852	1263	205.2
1,1,2-Trichloroethene		—	7.028	1315	230
Triethylamine	$(C_2H_5)_3N$	0 to 130	6.826	1161	205
Trimethylamine	$(CH_3)_3N$	-50 to 50	6.816	937.5	235
1,2,3-Trimethylbenzene	$(CH_3)_3C_6H_3$	—	7.041	1594	207.1
1,3,5-Trimethylbenzene	$(CH_3)_3C_6H_3$	—	7.07436	1569.62	209.58
Undecane	$CH_3(CH_2)_9CH_3$	15 to 100	7.3685	1803.90	208.32
Undecene-1	$CH_2CH(CH_2)_8CH_3$	—	6.9666	1562.5	189.74
Vinyl chloride	CH_2CHCl	-100 to 50	6.4971	783.4	230.0
Water	H_2O	0 to 60	8.1076	1750.3	235.0
		60 to 150	7.9668	1668.2	228.0
m-Xylene	$CH_3C_6H_4CH_3$	—	7.0091	1462.3	215.1

[a]Data taken from Reference 391.

APPENDIX H:
VAPOR PRESSURES OF WATER AT VARIOUS TEMPERATURES[a]

Temperature (°C)	Vapor pressure (mm Hg)	Temperature (°C)	Vapor pressure (mm Hg)	Temperature (°C)	Vapor pressure (mm Hg)
0	5.579	34	39.898	68	214.17
1	4.926	35	42.175	69	223.73
2	5.294	36	44.563	70	233.7
3	5.685	37	47.067	71	243.9
4	6.101	38	49.692	72	254.6
5	6.543	39	52.442	73	265.7
6	7.013	40	55.324	74	277.2
7	7.513	41	58.34	75	289.1
8	8.045	42	61.50	76	301.4
9	8.609	43	64.80	77	314.1
10	9.209	44	68.26	78	327.3
11	9.844	45	71.88	79	341.0
12	10.518	46	75.65	80	355.1
13	11.231	47	79.60	81	369.7
14	11.987	48	83.71	82	384.9
15	12.788	49	88.02	83	400.6
16	13.634	50	92.51	84	416.8
17	14.530	51	97.20	85	433.6
18	15.477	52	102.09	86	450.9
19	16.477	53	107.20	87	468.7
20	17.535	54	112.51	88	487.1
21	18.650	55	118.04	89	506.1
22	19.827	56	123.80	90	525.76
23	21.068	57	129.82	91	546.05
24	22.377	58	136.08	92	566.99
25	23.756	59	142.60	93	588.60
26	25.209	60	149.38	94	610.90
27	26.739	61	156.43	95	633.90
28	28.349	62	163.77	96	657.62
29	30.043	63	171.38	97	682.07
30	31.824	64	179.31	98	707.27
31	33.695	65	187.54	99	733.24
32	35.663	66	196.09	100	760.00
33	37.729	67	204.96	101	787.57

[a] Data taken from Reference 391.

APPENDIX I:
MASS OF WATER VAPOR IN SATURATED AIR

Temperature (°F)	(°C)	Mass (g of H_2O/m^3 of saturated mixture)	Temperature (°F)	(°C)	Mass (g of H_2O/m^3 of saturated mixture)
0	-17.8	1.229	60	15.6	13.27
2	-16.7	1.318	62	16.7	14.19
4	-15.6	1.439	64	17.8	15.17
6	-14.4	1.574	66	18.9	16.20
8	-13.3	1.698	68	20.0	17.30
10	-12.2	1.860	70	21.1	18.45
12	-11.1	2.046	72	22.2	19.69
14	-10.0	2.231	74	23.3	20.98
16	-8.9	2.439	76	24.4	22.34
18	-7.8	2.668	78	25.6	23.78
20	-6.7	2.938	80	26.7	25.31
22	-5.6	3.224	82	27.8	26.91
24	-4.4	3.517	84	28.9	28.60
26	-3.3	3.824	86	30.0	30.39
28	-2.2	4.147	88	31.1	32.27
30	-1.1	4.488	90	32.2	34.23
32	0.0	4.849	92	33.3	36.29
34	1.1	5.234	94	34.4	38.49
36	2.2	5.643	96	35.6	40.78
38	3.3	6.080	98	36.7	43.21
40	4.4	6.547	100	37.8	45.74
42	5.6	7.048	102	38.9	48.40
44	6.7	7.581	104	40.0	51.21
46	7.8	8.149	106	41.1	54.12
48	8.9	8.755	108	42.2	57.16
50	10.0	9.401	110	43.3	60.39
52	11.1	10.08	112	44.4	63.75
54	12.2	10.81	114	45.6	67.28
56	13.3	11.59	116	46.7	70.94
58	14.4	12.40	118	47.8	74.83

Temperature (°F)	(°C)	Mass (g of H_2O/m^3 of saturated mixture)	Temperature (°F)	(°C)	Mass (g of H_2O/m^3 of saturated mixture)
120	48.9	78.86	162	72.2	216.8
122	50.0	83.05	164	73.3	226.5
124	51.1	87.44	166	74.4	236.7
126	52.2	92.06	168	75.6	247.2
128	53.3	96.87	170	76.7	258.1
130	54.4	101.8	172	77.8	269.5
132	55.6	107.1	174	78.9	281.2
134	56.7	112.5	176	80.0	293.4
136	57.8	118.2	178	81.1	305.9
138	58.9	124.1	180	82.2	319.0
140	60.0	130.2	182	83.3	332.4
142	61.1	136.7	184	84.4	346.3
144	62.2	143.4	186	85.6	360.8
146	63.3	150.3	188	86.7	375.7
148	64.4	157.5	190	87.8	391.2
150	65.6	165.1	192	88.9	407.1
152	66.7	172.9	194	90.0	423.5
154	67.8	181.1	196	91.1	440.5
156	68.9	189.5	198	92.2	458.0
158	70.0	198.2	200	93.3	476.2
160	71.1	207.3			

APPENDIX J:
RELATIVE HUMIDITY FROM WET- AND DRY-BULB THERMOMETER READINGS[a]

This table gives the approximate relative humidity directly from a reading of the dry-bulb temperature, t_D, and the wet-bulb temperature, t_W, (both in °C) at a pressure of 74.27 cm Hg.

t_D \ $t_D - t_W$	0.2	0.4	0.6	0.8	1.0	1.2	1.4	1.6	1.8	2.0	2.2	2.4	2.6	2.8	3.0	3.2	3.4	3.6
-10	93	87	80	74	67	61	54	48	41	35	28	22	16	9	—	—	—	—
-9	94	88	81	75	69	63	57	51	45	39	33	27	21	15	9	—	—	—
-8	94	88	83	77	71	65	60	54	48	43	37	32	26	20	15	10	—	—
-7	95	89	84	78	73	67	62	57	52	46	41	36	31	25	20	15	10	5
-6	95	90	85	79	74	69	64	59	54	49	45	40	35	30	25	20	15	11
-5	95	90	86	81	76	71	66	62	57	52	48	43	39	34	29	25	20	16
-4	95	91	86	82	77	73	68	64	59	55	51	46	42	38	33	29	25	21
-3	96	91	87	82	78	74	70	66	62	57	53	49	45	41	37	33	29	25
-2	96	92	88	84	79	75	71	68	64	60	56	52	48	44	40	37	33	29
-1	96	92	88	84	81	77	73	69	66	62	58	54	51	47	43	40	36	33
0	96	93	89	85	81	78	74	71	67	64	60	57	53	50	46	43	40	36
1	97	93	90	86	83	80	76	73	70	66	63	59	56	53	49	46	43	40
2	97	93	90	87	84	81	78	74	71	68	65	62	59	55	52	49	46	43
3	97	94	91	88	84	82	78	76	73	70	67	64	61	58	55	52	49	46
4	97	94	91	88	85	82	79	77	74	71	68	65	62	60	57	54	51	48
5	97	94	91	88	86	83	80	77	75	72	69	67	64	61	58	56	53	51
6	97	94	92	89	86	84	81	78	76	73	70	68	65	63	60	58	55	53
7	97	95	92	89	87	84	82	79	77	74	72	69	67	64	62	59	57	54
8	97	95	92	90	87	85	82	80	77	75	73	70	68	65	63	61	58	56
9	98	95	93	90	88	85	83	81	78	76	74	71	69	67	64	62	60	58
10	98	95	93	90	88	86	83	81	79	77	74	72	70	68	66	63	61	59
11	98	95	93	91	89	86	84	82	80	78	75	73	71	69	67	65	62	60
12	98	96	93	91	89	87	85	82	80	78	76	74	72	70	68	66	64	62
13	98	96	93	91	89	87	85	83	81	79	77	75	73	71	69	67	65	63
14	98	96	94	92	90	88	86	84	82	79	78	76	74	72	70	68	66	64
15	98	96	94	92	90	88	86	84	82	80	78	76	74	73	71	69	67	65

	0.5	1.0	1.5	2.0	2.5	3.0	3.5	4.0	4.5	5.0	5.5	6.0	6.5	7.0	7.5	8.0	8.5	9.0	9.5
16	95	90	85	81	76	71	67	63	58	54	50	46	42	38	34	30	26	23	19
17	95	90	86	81	76	72	68	64	60	55	51	47	43	40	36	32	28	25	21
18	95	91	86	82	77	73	69	65	61	57	53	49	45	41	38	34	30	27	23
19	95	91	87	82	78	74	70	65	62	58	54	50	46	43	39	36	32	29	26
20	96	91	87	83	78	74	70	66	63	59	55	51	48	44	41	37	34	31	28
21	96	91	87	83	79	75	71	67	64	60	56	53	49	46	42	39	36	32	29
22	96	92	87	83	79	76	72	68	64	61	57	54	50	47	44	40	37	34	31
23	96	92	88	84	80	76	72	69	65	62	58	55	52	48	45	42	39	36	33
24	96	92	88	84	80	77	73	69	66	62	59	56	53	49	46	43	40	37	34
25	96	92	88	84	81	77	74	70	67	63	60	57	54	50	47	44	41	39	36
26	96	92	88	85	81	78	74	71	67	64	61	58	54	51	49	46	43	40	37
27	96	92	89	85	82	78	75	71	68	65	62	58	56	52	50	47	44	41	38
28	96	93	89	85	82	78	75	72	69	65	62	59	56	53	51	48	45	42	40
29	96	93	89	86	82	79	76	72	69	66	63	60	57	54	52	49	46	43	41
30	96	93	89	86	83	79	76	73	70	67	64	61	58	55	52	50	47	44	42
31	96	93	90	86	83	80	77	73	70	67	64	61	59	56	53	51	48	45	43
32	96	93	90	86	83	80	77	74	71	68	65	62	60	57	54	51	49	46	44
33	97	93	90	87	84	80	77	74	71	68	66	63	60	57	55	52	50	47	45
34	97	93	90	87	84	81	78	75	72	69	66	63	61	58	56	53	51	48	46
35	97	94	90	87	84	81	78	75	72	69	67	64	61	59	56	54	51	49	47
36	97	94	90	87	84	81	78	75	73	70	67	64	62	59	57	54	52	50	48
37	97	94	91	87	84	82	79	76	73	70	68	65	63	60	58	55	53	51	48
38	97	94	91	88	84	82	79	76	74	71	68	66	63	61	58	56	54	51	49
39	97	94	91	88	85	82	79	77	74	71	69	66	64	61	59	57	54	52	50
40	97	94	91	88	85	82	80	77	74	72	69	67	64	62	59	57	54	53	51

[a] Data taken from Reference 63.

t_D-t_w \ t_D	3.8	4.0	4.5	5.0	5.5	6.0	6.5	7.0	7.5	8.0	8.5	9.0	9.5	10.0	10.5	11.0
-10																
-9																
-8																
-7																
-6	6	7														
-5	11	12														
-4	17	17														
-3	21	22	8													
-2	25	26	12													
-1	29	26	17	8												
0	33	29	21	13	5											
1	36	33	25	17	10											
2	40	37	29	22	14	7										
3	43	40	33	26	19	12	5									
4	46	43	36	29	22	16	9									
5	48	45	39	33	26	20	13	7								
6	50	48	41	35	29	24	17	11	5							
7	52	50	44	38	32	26	21	15	10							
8	54	51	46	40	35	29	24	19	14	8						
9	55	53	48	42	37	32	27	22	17	12	7					
10	57	55	50	44	39	34	29	24	20	15	10	6				
11	58	56	51	46	41	36	32	27	22	18	13	9	5			
12	60	58	53	48	43	39	34	29	25	21	16	12	8			
13	61	59	54	50	45	41	36	32	28	23	19	15	11	7		
14	62	60	56	51	47	42	38	34	30	26	22	18	14	10	6	
15	63	61	57	53	48	44	40	36	32	27	24	20	16	13	9	6

	10.0	10.5	11.0	11.5	12.0	12.5	13.0	13.5	14.0	14.5	15.0	16.0	17.0	18.0	19.0	20.0
16	15	12	8	5	—	—	—	—	—	—	—	—	—	—	—	—
17	18	14	11	8	7	—	—	—	—	—	—	—	—	—	—	—
18	20	17	14	10	10	7	—	—	—	—	—	—	—	—	—	—
19	22	19	16	13	12	9	6	—	—	—	—	—	—	—	—	—
20	24	21	18	15	14	12	9	6	—	—	—	—	—	—	—	—
21	26	23	20	17	17	14	11	8	6	—	—	—	—	—	—	—
22	28	25	22	19	19	16	13	11	8	6	—	—	—	—	—	—
23	30	27	24	21	20	18	15	13	10	8	5	—	—	—	—	—
24	31	29	26	23	22	20	17	15	12	10	8	—	—	—	—	—
25	33	30	28	25	24	21	19	17	14	12	10	—	—	—	—	—
26	34	32	29	26	26	23	21	18	16	14	12	5	—	—	—	—
27	36	33	31	28	27	24	22	20	18	16	13	7	—	—	—	—
28	37	34	32	29	28	25	24	22	19	17	15	9	5	—	—	—
29	38	36	33	31	29	26	25	23	21	19	17	11	7	—	—	—
30	39	37	35	32	30	28	26	24	22	20	18	13	9	5	—	—
31	40	38	36	33	31	29	27	25	24	22	20	14	11	7	—	—
32	41	39	37	35	32	30	28	26	25	23	21	16	12	9	5	—
33	42	40	38	36	33	31	29	27	26	24	22	17	14	10	7	—
34	43	41	39	37	35	32	30	28	27	25	23	19	15	12	8	5
35	44	42	40	38	36	34	32	30	28	26	24	20	17	13	10	7
36	45	43	41	39	37	35	33	31	29	27	25	21	18	15	11	8
37	46	44	42	40	38	36	34	32	30	28	26	23	19	16	13	10
38	47	45	43	41	39	37	35	33	31	29	27	24	20	17	14	11
39	48	46	43	42	39	38	36	34	32	30	28	25	22	18	15	12
40	48	46	44	42	40	38	36	35	33	31	29	26	23	20	16	14

APPENDIX K:

Definition of Symbols

A	Cross-sectional area
A, B, C	Constants for vapor-pressure calculations
C	Concentration
$c_{a, b, ..., n}$	Concentration of components a, b, ..., n
C_D	Discharge coefficient
c_S	Concentration of a solution
c_0	Initial concentration
D	Diffusion coefficient
d	Diameter
E_P	Permeation activation energy
F	Faraday's constant (96,489 Coul/mole)
g	Acceleration due to gravity
H_P	Per cent humidity
H_R	Relative humidity
I	Current
K	Proportionality constant
K_H	Ratio of specific heat at constant pressure to specific heat at constant volume
L	Length
M	Molecular weight
m_A	Molecular weight of a diluent gas
m_B	Molecular weight of a diffusing gas
N	Yield factor
n	Number of moles
n_T	Thread periodicity of a lead screw
n_W	Number of revolutions of a lead screw
P	Total pressure
$p_{a, b, ..., n}$	Partial pressure of components a, b,..., n
p_D	Pressure of a diluent gas
p_G	Gas-permeability constant
p_R	Permeation rate
p_V	Pressure of a diffusing vapor
p_W	Partial vapor pressure of water
p_{WS}	Partial vapor pressure of water at saturation
p_0	Initial pressure
Q	Total flow rate of a gas
Q_m	Mass flow rate of a gas

$q_{a, b, \ldots, n}$	Flow rate of components a, b,..., n
q_D	Flow rate of a diluent gas
q_d	Rate of diffusion of a gas
q_E	Rate of electrolytic gas production
q_G	Volume of gas dispensed
q_L	Volume of liquid dispensed
R	Molar gas constant
r	Capillary flow resistance
S	Solubility constant
T	Absolute temperature
t	Ordinary temperature
t_D	Dry-bulb temperature
t_W	Wet-bulb temperature
$\bar{u}$	Average velocity of a gas
V	Total volume
v	Volume of 1 mole of ideal gas under standard conditions
v_A	Actual gas volume
$v_{a, b, \ldots, n}$	Volume of components a, b,..., n
v_C	Volume of a contaminant gas
v_D	Volume of a diluent gas
v_I	Ideal gas volume
v_L	Volume of a liquid
v_S	Volume of a syringe
v_s	Volume of a solution
v_W	Volume of gas withdrawn
W	Weight
X	Mole fraction
Z	Valence electron number
z	Number of electrons required to liberate 1 mole of gas
η	Viscosity of a gas
κ	Compressibility
ρ	Density of a gas or liquid
ρ_A	Actual gas density
ρ_{air}	Density of air
ρ_I	Ideal gas density
ρ_L	Density of a liquid
τ	Time

References

1. Perry, J. H. *Chemical Engineers Handbook* (New York: McGraw-Hill Book Company, Inc., 1950).
2. Hammond, W. A. *Drierite, the Versatile Desiccant, and Its Applications in the Drying of Solids, Liquids, and Gases* (Columbus, Ohio: The Stoneman Press, 1958).
3. Trusell, F., and H. Diehl. Anal. Chem. 35, 674 (1963).
4. Skoog, D. A., and D. M. West. *Fundamentals of Analytical Chemistry* (New York: Holt, Rinehart & Winston, Inc., 1963).
5. Hougen, O. A., and F. W. Dodge. *The Drying of Gases* (Ann Arbor, Michigan: Edwards Brothers, Inc., 1947).
6. Morton, A. A. *Laboratory Techniques in Organic Chemistry* (New York: McGraw-Hill Book Company, Inc., 1938).
7. Nonhebel, G. *Gas Purification Processes* (London: George Newnes, Ltd., 1964).
8. Catalog No. 200, Permanent Filter Corporation, Compton, California.
9. Bulletin Nos. FM-1100, -1200, and -1300, Huyck Metals Company, Milford, Connecticut.
10. Bulletin No. 1, Sintered Specialties, Janesville, Wisconsin.
11. Brochure, General Electric Company, Detroit, Michigan.
12. Brochure, Pall Corporation, Glen Cove, New York.
13. 1969 catalog, Pure Aire Corporation of America, Van Nuys, California.
14. Brochure, Arthur H. Thomas Company, Philadelphia, Pennsylvania.
15. Catalog No. MF-64, Millipore Corporation, Bedford, Massachusetts.
16. Brochure, The Dexter Corporation, Windsor Locks, Connecticut.
17. Barnebey, H. L. *Heating, Piping, Air Conditioning* 30, 153 (1958).
18. Kusnetz, H. L., B. E. Saltzman, and M. E. Lanier. Am. Ind. Hyg. Assoc. J. 21, 361 (1960).
19. Catalog No. 600, King Engineering Corporation, Ann Arbor, Michigan.
20. Bulletin No. 118, R. P. Adams Company, Inc., Buffalo, New York.
21. Circular No. 1066, Wilkerson Corporation, Englewood, Colorado.

22. Bulletin No. 200, Dollinger Corporation, Rochester, New York.

23. Form No. 101-E, Deltech Engineering, Inc., New Castle, Delaware.

24. *Respiratory Protective Devices Manual* (Ann Arbor, Michigan: Braun and Brumfield, Inc., 1963), Chapter 5.

25. Catalog No. P-900, Warren E. Collins, Inc., Braintree, Massachusetts.

26. Bulletin No. 207.1, American Meter Controls, Philadelphia, Pennsylvania.

27. Catalog AG-1, American Meter Controls, Philadelphia, Pennsylvania.

28. Catalog LPG-4A, American Meter Controls, Philadelphia, Pennsylvania.

29. Bulletin A1M-207, American Meter Controls, Philadelphia, Pennsylvania.

30. Powell, C. H., and A. D. Hosey, Eds. *The Industrial Environment–Its Evaluation and Control* (Washington, D. C.: U.S. Government Printing Office, 1965).

31. Ower, E., and R. C. Pankhurst. *The Measurement of Air Flow*, 4th ed. (Elmsford, New York: Pergamon Publishing Company, 1966).

32. *Industrial Ventilation*, 10th ed. (Ann Arbor, Michigan: Edwards Brothers, Inc., 1968).

33. Brandt, A. D. *Industrial Health Engineering* (New York: John Wiley & Sons, Inc., 1947).

34. Barr, G. J. Sci. Inst. **11**, 321 (1934).

35. 1969 Catalog, Emerson Electric Company, Hatfield, Pennsylvania.

36. Kusnetz, H. Am. Ind. Hyg. Assoc. J. **21**, 340 (1960).

37. Levy, A. J. Sci. Instr. **41**, 449 (1964).

38. Noble, F. W., K. Abel, and P. W. Cook. Anal. Chem. **37**, 1631 (1965).

39. *Instrument Calibrates Low Gas-Rate Flowmeters*, technical brief No. 65–10137, National Aeronautics and Space Administration, Houston, Texas, 1965.

40. Hunter, J. J. J. Sci. Instr. **42**, 175 (1965).

41. Frisone, G. J. Chemist-Analyst **54**, 56 (1965).

42. Czubryt, J. J., and H. D. Gesser. J. Gas Chromatog. **6**, 528 (1968).

43. Van Swaay, M. V. J. Chromatog. **12**, 99 (1963).

44. Brief, R. S., and R. G. Confer. Am. Ind. Hyg. Assoc. J. **30**, 576 (1969).

45. *Standard Methods for Measurement of Gaseous Fuel Samples*, publication No. ASTM-D-1071-55, American Society for Testing and Materials, Philadelphia, Pennsylvania, 1963.

46. Bulletin No. TS-63110-3, Precision Scientific Company, Chicago, Illinois.

47. Data sheet No. LM.1, Parkinson-Cowan Measurement, Stretford, Manchester, England.

48. Catalog No. EG-40, American Meter Controls, Philadelphia, Pennsylvania.

49. Instr. Control Systems **27**, 101 (1970).

50. Anal. Chem. **41**, 176LG (1969).

51. Instr. Control Systems **42**, 100 (1969).

52. Instr. Control Systems **42**, 115 (1969).
53. Fairchild, E. J., and H. E. Stokinger. Am. Ind. Hyg. Assoc. J. **19**, 171 (1958).
54. Nash, D. L. Appl. Spectry. **21**, 126 (1967).
55. Martin, J. J. Chem. Eng. Progr. **45**, 338 (1949).
56. Haenel, R. D. Instr. Control Systems **41**, 127 (1968).
57. Hougen, J. O. Instruments **26**, 1716 (1953).
58. Gilmont, R., and B. Roccanova. Instr. Control Systems **39**, 89 (1966).
59. Polentz, L. M. Instr. Control Systems **34**, 1048 (1961).
60. Coleman, M. C. Trans. Inst. Chem. Engrs. (London) **34**, 339 (1956).
61. Hersch, P. A. J. Air Pollution Control Assoc. **19**, 164 (1969).
62. Jentzsch, D. J. Gas Chromatogr. **5**, 226 (1967).
63. Weast, R. C., S. M. Selby, and C. D. Hodgman, Eds. *Handbook of Chemistry and Physics*, 46th ed. (Cleveland: The Chemical Rubber Company, 1965).
64. Hatch, T., H. Warren, and P. Drinker. J. Ind. Hyg. Tox. **14**, 301 (1932).
65. Page, R. T. Ind. Eng. Chem. **7**, 355 (1935).
66. Collins, W. T. *A Gravimetric Standard for Primary Gas Flow Measurements*, report No. K-L-6181, Oak Ridge National Laboratory, Oak Ridge, Tennessee, 1967.
67. Lodge, J. P., J. B. Pate, B. E. Ammons, and G. A. Swanson. J. Air Pollution Control Assoc. **16**, 197 (1966).
68. Pinkerton, M. K., J. M. Lauer, P. Diamond, and A. A. Tamas. Am. Ind. Hyg. Assoc. J. **24**, 239 (1963).
69. Malkova, E. M., and Z. T. Kezina. Meas. Tech. (USSR) (English Transl.) **1961**, 921.
70. Axelrod, H. D., J. H. Carey, J. E. Bonelli, and J. P. Lodge. Anal. Chem. **41**, 1856 (1969).
71. Corn. M., and W. Bell. Am. Ind. Hyg. Assoc. J. **24**, 502 (1963).
72. Imada, M. R., and E. Jeung. "Integrated Gas Sampling Techniques Utilizing Critical Orifices," paper presented at the 8th Conference on Methods in Air Pollution and Industrial Hygiene Studies, Kaiser Center, Oakland, California, February 6–8, 1967.
73. Silverman, L., J. J. Fitzgerald, W. A. Burgess, M. Corn, and F. Stein. *Respiratory Protective Equipment*, report No. 9322, Harvard University, Cambridge, Massachusetts, 1960.
74. Wartburg, A. F., J. B. Pate, and J. P. Lodge. Environ. Sci. Technol. **3**, 767 (1969).
75. Saltzman, B. E., and N. Gilbert. Am. Ind. Hyg. Assoc. J. **20**, 379 (1959).
76. Avera, C. B. Rev. Sci. Instr. **32**, 985 (1961).
77. Saltzman, B. E. Anal. Chem. **33**, 1100 (1961).
78. Saltzman, B. E., A. F. Wartburg. Anal. Chem. **37**, 1261 (1965).
79. Bostrom, C. E. Int. J. Air Water Pollut. **9**, 333 (1965).
80. Paty, L. Vacuum **7–8**, 80 (1957–8).

81. Guthrie, D. G. *A Gas Blender for Minor Components at Concentrations Between 10 and 1000 v.p.m.*, report No. 270(D), United Kingdom Atomic Energy Authority, London, 1962.
82. Brochure, Mott Metallurgical Corporation, Farmington, Connecticut.
83. Hoff, M. Instr. Control Systems 42, 83 (1969).
84. Bulletin No. N16-2, Thermo-Systems, Inc., St. Paul, Minnesota.
85. Bulletin No. 1000, Flow Corporation, Watertown, Massachusetts.
86. Arya, S. P. S., and E. J. Plate. Instr. Control Systems 42, 87 (1969).
87. Bulletin No. 1350, Thermo-Systems, Inc., St. Paul, Minnesota.
88. Bulletin No. 1050, Thermo-Systems, Inc., St. Paul, Minnesota.
89. Struckmeier, H. Staub 28, 28 (1968).
90. Bulletin No. 505A, Technology Versatronics Inc., Yellow Springs, Ohio.
91. Specification sheet 508A, Hastings-Raydist, Hampton, Virginia.
92. Brochure, Matheson Company, Inc., Cucamonga, California.
93. Hama, G. M. Am. Ind. Hyg. Assoc. J. 19, 477 (1958).
94. Stapler, M. Instr. Control Systems 35, 97 (1962).
95. Brochure, Ramapo Instrument Company, Inc., Bloomingdale, New Jersey.
96. Lovelock, J. E., and E. M. Wasilewska. J. Sci. Instr. 26, 367 (1949).
97. Fox, E. A., and V. E. Gex. J. Air Pollution Control Assoc. 7, 60 (1957).
98. Byrd, J. F. J. Air Pollution Control Assoc. 7, 58 (1957).
99. Benforado, D. M., W. J. Rotella, and D. L. Horton. J. Air Pollution Control Assoc. 19, 101 (1969).
100. Cotabish, H. N., P. W. McConnaughey, and H. C. Messer. Am. Ind. Hyg. Assoc. J. 22, 393 (1961).
101. Williams, H. P., and J. D. Winefordner. J. Gas Chromatog. 4, 271 (1966).
102. DeGrazio, R. P. J. Gas Chromotog. 6, 468 (1968).
103. Thuman, W. C. *Development of Technology for Production, Sampling and Assay of Simulated Atmospheres in Closed Chamber*, unnumbered report, Stanford Research Institute, Palo Alto, California, 1958.
104. Brief, R. S., and F. W. Church. Am. Ind. Hyg. Assoc. J. 21, 239 (1960).
105. Campbell, E. E., M. F. Milligan, and H. M. Miller. Am. Ind. Hyg. Assoc, J. 20, 138 (1959).
106. Leonardos, G., D. Kendall, and N. Barnard. J. Air Pollution Control Assoc. 19, 91 (1969).
107. Baretta, E. D., R. D. Stewart, and J. E. Mutchler. Am. Ind. Hyg. Assoc. J. 30, 537 (1969).
108. Stead, F. M., and G. J. Taylor. J. Ind. Hyg. Tox. 29, 408 (1947).
109. Van Sandt, W., V. Santomassimo, and R. Taylor. "Determination of Dilution of Vapors in Calibration Bottles by Infrared Analysis," in *Hazards Control Quarterly Report*, report No. UCRL-7450, Lawrence Radiation Laboratory, Livermore, California, 1963.

110. Apol, A. G., W. A. Cook, and E. F. Lawrence. Am. Ind. Hyg. Assoc. J. 27, 149 (1966).
111. Morley, M. J., and B. D. Tebbens. Am. Ind. Hyg. Assoc. J. 14, 303 (1953).
112. McCaldin, R. O., and E. R. Hendrickson. Am. Ind. Hyg. Assoc. J. 20, 509 (1959).
113. Catalog No. H-70, Hamilton Company, Whittier, California.
114. 1961 catalog, Scientific Products, Inc., Detroit, Michigan.
115. 1969 catalog, Cole-Parmer Instrument Company, Chicago, Illinois.
116. Lodge, J. P., J. B. Pate, and H. A. Huitt. Chemist-Analyst 52, 53 (1963).
117. Setterlind, A. N. Am. Ind. Hyg. Assoc. J. 14, 114 (1953).
118. *Matheson Gas Data Handbook*, 4th ed. (East Rutherford, New Jersey: Matheson Company, Inc., 1966).
119. 1968 catalog, Airco Industrial Gases, New York, New York.
120. Feldstein, J., J. D. Coons, H. C. Johnson, and J. E. Yocom. Am. Ind. Hyg. Assoc. J. 20, 374 (1959).
121. Roccanova, B. "Present State of the Art of the Preparation of Gaseous Standards," paper presented at the Conference on Analytical Chemistry and Spectroscopy, Pittsburgh, Pennsylvania, 1968.
122. Catalog No. G-67, Cole-Parmer Instrument Company, Chicago, Illinois.
123. Crawford, R. W. *An Automatic, Variable-Volume, Gas Dispenser*, report No. UCID-15138, revision 1, Lawrence Radiation Laboratory, Livermore, California, 1965.
124. Silverman, L. "Experimental Test Methods," in P. L. Magill, F. R. Holden, and C. Ackley, Eds., *Air Pollution Handbook* (New York: McGraw-Hill Book Company, Inc., 1956).
125. Vango, S. P. Chemist-Analyst 52, 53 (1963).
126. Urone, P., J. B. Evans, and C. Mo. Noyes. Anal. Chem. 37, 1104 (1965).
127. Russell, S. Am. Ind. Hyg. Assoc. J. 25, 359 (1964).
128. Mullet, C. W. Gas 37, 59 (1961).
129. Langer, A. Rev. Sci. Instr. 18, 101 (1947).
130. Roberts, R. M., and J. J. Madison. Anal. Chem. 29, 1555 (1957).
131. Hanson, D. N., and A. Maimoni. Anal. Chem. 31, 158 (1959).
132. Back, R. A., N. J. Friswell, J. C. Boden, and J. M. Parsons. J. Chromatog. Sci. 7, 708 (1969).
133. Stewart, R. D. Am. Ind. Hyg. Assoc. J. 22, 252 (1961).
134. Brown, J. R., and E. Mastromatteo. Am. Ind. Hyg. Assoc. J. 25, 560 (1964).
135. Brief, R. S., R. S. Ajemian, and R. G. Confer. Am. Ind. Hyg. Assoc. J. 28, 21 (1967).
136. Buchberg, H., and K. W. Wilson. J. Air Pollution Control Assoc. 8, 285 (1959).
137. Buchberg, H., K. W. Wilson, and R. P. Lipkis. *Preliminary Design Study—Air Resource Test Facilities*, report No. 56–59, University of California, Los Angeles, California, 1956.

138. Silver, S. D.   J. Lab. Clin. Med. **31**, 1153 (1946).
139. Gill, W. E.   Am. Ind. Hyg. Assoc. J. **21**, 87 (1960).
140. Caplan, P. E.   "Calibration of Air Sampling Instruments," in *Air Sampling Instruments for Evaluation of Atmospheric Contaminants* (Cincinnati: American Conference of Governmental Industrial Hygienists, 1966).
141. Fultyn, R. V.   Am. Ind. Hyg. Assoc. J. **22**, 49 (1961).
142. Groth, R. H., and T. B. Doyle.   J. Gas Chromatog. **6**, 138 (1968).
143. Wohlers, H. C., N. M. Trieff, H. Newstein, and W. Stevens.   Atmos. Environ. **1**, 121 (1967).
144. Sherberger, R. F., G. P. Happ, F. A. Miller, and D. W. Fassett.   Am. Ind. Hyg. Assoc. J. **19**, 494 (1958).
145. Lodge, J. P.   "Production of Controlled Test Atmospheres," *Air Pollution* A. C. Stern, Ed. (New York: Academic Press, 1962).
146. Conner, W. D., and J. S. Nader.   Am. Ind. Hyg. Assoc. J. **25**, 291 (1964).
147. Williams, H. P., C. V. Overfield, and J. D. Winefordner.   J. Gas Chromatog. **5**, 511 (1967).
148. Lacy, J., and K. G. Woolmington.   Analyst **86**, 547 (1961).
149. Baker, R. A., and R. C. Doerr.   Int. J. Air Water Pollut. **2**, 142 (1959).
150. Welch, A. F., and J. P. Terry.   Am. Ind. Hyg. Assoc. J. **21**, 316 (1960).
151. Vanderkolk, A. L., and D. E. Van Farowe.   Am. Ind. Hyg. Assoc. J. **26**, 321 (1965).
152. Altshuller, A. P., A. F. Wartburg, I. R. Cohen, and S. F. Sleva.   Int. J. Air Water Pollut. **6**, 75 (1962).
153. Pate, J. B., J. P. Lodge, and M. P. Neary.   Anal. Chem. Acta **28**, 341 (1963).
154. Cederlof, R., M. Edfors, L. Friberg, and T. Lindvall.   J. Air Pollution Control Assoc. **16**, 92 (1966).
155. Wilson, K. W., and H. Buchberg.   Ind. Eng. Chem. **50**, 1705 (1958).
156. Simonds, H. R., and J. M. Church.   *A Concise Guide to Plastics*, 2nd ed. (New York: Reinhold Publishing Company, 1963).
157. Brochure, Calibrated Instruments, Inc., New York, New York.
158. Brochure, Analytical Specialities, Inc., Ann Arbor, Michigan.
159. Private communication from V. C. Santomassimo, Lawrence Radiation Laboratory, Livermore, California.
160. Urone, P., H. Lutsep, C. M. Noyes, and J. F. Parcher.   Environ. Sci. Technol. **2**, 611 (1968).
161. Clemons, C. A., and A. D. Altshuller.   J. Air Pollution Control Assoc. **14**, 407 (1964).
162. Bulletin No. 69022, Precision Gas Products, Inc., Linden, New Jersey.
163. Bulletin No. 7167, Scott Research Laboratories, Inc., San Bernardino, California.
164. Opler, A., and E. S. Smith.   Anal. Chem. **25**, 686 (1953).
165. French patent 1,087,140.

166. Shannon, D. W. "Gas Chromatograph," in *Quarterly Progress Report, Metallurgy Research Operation, April, May, June, 1964,* report No. HW-82651, General Electric Company, Richland, Washington (1964).

167. Ruby, E. D. *An Apparatus for the Preparation of Standard Gas Mixtures Containing Trace Level Components,* report No. RFP-358, Dow Chemical Company, Rocky Flats, Colorado (1964).

168. Baker, W. J., and T. L. Zinn. Perkin-Elmer Instrument News 11, 1 (1960).

169. Zdrojewski, A., and J. L. Monkman. Am. Ind. Hyg. Assoc. J. 30, 650 (1969).

170. Batt, L., and F. R. Cruickshank. J. Chem. Soc. (London) A2, 261 (1967).

171. Shepherd, M. Anal. Chem. 19, 77 (1947).

172. Hill, D. W. Brit. J. Appl. Phys. 12, 410 (1961).

173. Bochkova, O. P., and E. Y. Shreyder. *Spectroscopic Analysis of Gas Mixtures* (New York: Academic Press, 1965).

174. Hughes, E. E., and W. D. Dorko. Anal. Chem. 40, 750 (1968).

175. Gurvich, V. S. Izv. Sibirsk. Otd. Akad. Nauk SSSR 1969, 165.

176. Miller, J. E., A. J. Carroll, and D. E. Emerson. *Preparation of Primary Standard Gas Mixtures for Analytical Instruments,* report No. 6674, U.S. Bureau of Mines, Washington, D.C. (1965).

177. Altshuller, A. P., and A. F. Wartburg. Appl. Spectry. 15, 67 (1961).

178. DeGrazio, R. P., and R. G. Auge. *Evaluation of a Gas Mixing System,* report No. RFP-1143, Dow Chemical Company, Rocky Flats, Colorado (1968).

179. King, W. H., and G. D. Dupre. Anal. Chem. 41, 1936 (1969).

180. Irish, D. D., and E. M. Adams. Ind. Med. Surg. 1, 1 (1940).

181. Box, W. D. Am. Ind. Hyg. Assoc. J. 24, 618 (1963).

182. Jellinek, H. H. G., and F. J. Kryman. Environ. Sci. Technol. 1, 658 (1967).

183. Birks, N., and T. Flatley. J. Sci. Instr. 2, 436 (1969).

184. Bate, G. C., A. D'Aoust, and D. T. Canvin. Plant Physiol. 44, 1122 (1969).

185. Adams, D. F. J. Air Pollution Control Assoc. 13, 88 (1963).

186. Mastromatteo, E., A. M. Fisher, H. Christie, and H. Danziger. Am. Ind. Hyg. Assoc. J. 21, 394 (1960).

187. Angely, L., E. Levart, G. Guiochon and G. Peslerbe. Anal. Chem. 41, 1456 (1969).

188. Haun, C. C., E. H. Vernot, D. L. Geiger, and J. M. McNerney. Am. Ind. Hyg. Assoc. J. 30, 551 (1969).

189. Pecora, L. J. Am. Ind. Hyg. Assoc, J. 20, 235 (1959).

190. Lester, D., L. A. Greenberg, and W. R. Adams. Am. Ind. Hyg. Assoc. J. 24, 265 (1963).

191. Zocchi, F. J. Gas Chromatog. 6, 100 (1968).

192. Levinskas, G. J., M. R. Paslian, and W. R. Bleckman. Am. Ind. Hyg. Assoc. J. 19, 46 (1958).

193. Murphy, S. D., C. E. Ulrich, S. H. Frankowitz, and C. Xintaras. Am. Ind. Hyg. Assoc. J. **25**, 246 (1964).

194. Duckworth, S., D. Levaggi, and J. Lim. J. Air Pollution Control Assoc. **13**, 429 (1963).

195. Dalhamn, T., and L. Strandberg. Int. J. Air Water Pollut. **4**, 154 (1961).

196. Malanchuk, M. Am. Ind. Hyg. Assoc. J. **28**, 76 (1967).

197. Barr, G. J. Sci. Instr. **11**, 321 (1934).

198. Wilby, F. V. J. Air Pollution Control Assoc. **19**, 96 (1969).

199. Zolty, S., and M. J. Prager. J. Gas Chromatog. **5**, 533 (1967).

200. Sordelli, D. Riv. Combust. **13**, 122 (1959).

201. Schnelle, P. D. Instr. Soc. Am. J. **4**, 128 (1957).

202. Troy, D. J. Anal. Chem. **27**, 1217 (1955).

203. Cummings, W. G., and M. W. Redfearn. Chem. Ind. (London) **1950**, 809 (1957).

204. Private communication from K. K. Butterfield, University of California, Berkeley, California.

205. Rogoff, J. M. J. Lab. Clin. Med. **25**, 853 (1939).

206. Saltzman, B. E. Am. Ind. Hyg. Assoc. J. **16**, 121 (1955).

207. Bulletin No. 5075, Davis Instruments, North Charlottesville, Virginia.

208. Sunderman, F. W., J. F. Kincaid, W. Kooch, and E. A. Bermelin. Am. J. Pathol. **26**, 1211 (1956).

209. Nelson, G. O., and K. S. Griggs. *A Precision Dynamic Method for Producing Known Concentrations of Gas and Solvent Vapor in Air*, report No. UCRL-70394, Lawrence Radiation Laboratory, Livermore, California (1967).

210. Nelson, G. O., and K. S. Griggs. Rev. Sci. Instr. **39**, 927 (1968).

211. Lester, D., and W. R. Adams. Am. Ind. Hyg. Assoc. J. **26**, 562 (1965).

212. Amdur, M. O., R. Z. Schulz, and P. Drinker. Arch. Ind. Hyg. Occup. Med. **5**, 318 (1952).

213. Jones, B. W., S. A. Jones, and M. B. Neuworth. Ind. Eng. Chem. **44**, 2233 (1952).

214. Hill, D. W., and H. A. Newell. J. Sci. Instr. **42**, 783 (1965).

215. Torkelson, T. R., F. Oyen, and V. K. Rowe. Am. Ind. Hyg. Assoc. J. **22**, 354 (1961).

216. Saltzman, B. E. Anal. Chem. **26**, 1949 (1954).

217. Fraust, C. L., and E. R. Hermann. Am. Ind. Hyg. Assoc. J. **27**, 68 (1966).

218. Kuczynski, E. R. Environ. Sci. Technol. **1**, 68 (1967).

219. Rowe, V. K., T. Wujkowski, M. A. Wolf, S. E. Sadek, and R. D. Stewart. Am. Ind. Hyg. Assoc. J. **24**, 541 (1963).

220. Bulletin No. 900, Harvard Apparatus Company, Inc., Millis, Massachusetts.

221. Diggle, W. M., and J. C. Gage. Analyst **78**, 473 (1953).

222. Schoen, D. Instr. Control Systems **42**, 165 (1969).
223. Data sheet No. DVR-650, Metron Instruments, Inc., Denver, Colorado.
224. Kuczynski, E. R. J. Air Pollution Control Assoc. **13**, 435 (1963).
225. Jacobson, K. H., W. E. Rinehart, H. J. Wheelwright, M. A. Ross, J. L. Papin, R. C. Daly, E. A. Greene, and W. A. Groff. Am. Ind. Hyg. Assoc. J. **19**, 91 (1958).
226. Weeks, M. H., T. O. Downing, N. P. Musselman, T. R. Carson, and W. A. Groff. Am. Ind. Hyg. Assoc. J. **21**, 374 (1960).
227. Nelson, G. O., W. Van Sandt, and P. E. Barry. Am. Ind. Hyg. Assoc. J. **26**, 388 (1965.).
228. Pozzani, U. C., C. S. Weil, and C. P. Carpenter. Am. Ind. Hyg. Assoc. J. **20**, 364 (1959).
229. Charnley, A., G. L. Isles, and J. S. Rowlinson. J. Sci. Instr. **31**, 145 (1954).
230. Nelson, G. O. *A Simplified Method for Producing Known Concentrations of Mercury Vapor in Air*, report No. UCRL-71481, Lawrence Radiation Laboratory, Livermore, California (1969).
231. Brochure, Clayborn Labs Inc., Santa Ana, California.
232. Gage, J. C. J. Sci. Instr. **30**, 25 (1953).
233. Clayton, J. W., H. Sherman, S. D. Morrison, J. R. Barnes, and D. B. Hood. Am. Ind. Hyg. Assoc. J. **27**, 332 (1966).
234. Hill, D. W., and H. A. Newell. Nature **205**, 593 (1965).
235. Fanney, J. H. Am. Ind. Hyg. Assoc. J. **24**, 245 (1963).
236. Dambrauskas, T., and W. A. Cook. Am. Ind. Hyg. Assoc. J. **24**, 568 (1963).
237. Silverman, L., and G. R. Gardner. Am. Ind. Hyg. Assoc. J. **26**, 97 (1965).
238. Nelson, G. O. Am. Ind. Hyg. Assoc. J. **29**, 586 (1958).
239. Nelson, G. O. Appl. Spectry. **23**, 133 (1969).
240. Private communication from R. D. Taylor, Lawrence Radiation Laboratory, Livermore, California.
241. Yant, W. P., and F. E. Frey. Ind. Eng. Chem. **17**, 692 (1925).
242. Hersch, P., C. J. Sambucetti, and R. Deuringer. "Electrolytic Calibration of Gas Monitors," paper presented at the 9th National Instrument Symposium, Houston, Texas, 1963.
243. Brochure, Sage Instruments, Inc., White Plains, New York.
244. Bulletin No. 540, Harvard Apparatus Company, Inc., Illis, Massachusetts.
245. Sayers, R. R., W. P. Yant, C. P. Waite, and F. A. Patty. Public Health Rept. (U.S.) **45**, 225 (1930).
246. Brubach, H. F. Rev. Sci. Instr. **18**, 363 (1947).
247. Goetz, A., and T. Kallai. Am. Ind. Hyg. Assoc. J. **24**, 453 (1963).
248. Rossano, A. T., and H. B. H. Cooper. J. Air Pollution Control Assoc. **13**, 518 (1963).
249. Calcote, H. F. Anal. Chem. **22**, 1058 (1950).

250. Hersch, P., and J. E. Whittle.   J. Sci. Instr. **35**, 32 (1958).

251. Lundsted, L. G., A. B. Ash, and N. L. Koslin.   Anal. Chem. **22**, 626 (1950).

252. Tokiwa, Y., and E. R. DeVera.   "The Woesthoff Gas Dosing Apparatus," paper presented at the 8th Conference on Methods in Air Pollution and Industrial Hygiene Studies, Oakland, California, 1967.

253. Axelrod, H. D., J. H. Carey, J. E. Bonelli, and J. P. Lodge.   Anal. Chem. **41**, 1856 (1969).

254. Axelrod, H. D., J. B. Pate, W. R. Barchet, and J. P. Lodge.   Atmos. Environ. **4**, 209 (1970).

255. Smith, S. B., and R. J. Grant.   *A Non-Selective Collector for Sampling Gaseous Air Pollutants*, report No. NP-8-193, U.S. Public Health Service, Cincinnati, Ohio (1960).

256. Nader, J. S.   Am. Ind. Hyg. Assoc. J. **19**, 1 (1958).

257. Devaux, P., and G. Guiochon.   Bull. Soc. Chim. France **1966**, 1404.

258. Dravnieks, A., and B. K. Krotoszynski.   Gas Chromatog. **6**, 144 (1968).

259. Fortun, J. M. H.   Anal. Chim. Acta **15**, 521 (1956).

260. Altshuller, A. P., and I. R. Cohen.   Anal. Chem. **32**, 802 (1960).

261. McKelvey, J. M., and H. E. Hoelscher.   Anal. Chem. **29**, 123 (1957).

262. Mgalobleshvili, K. D.   Geofiz. Apparat. **1968** (35) 164.

263. Private communication from C. B. Avera, Jr., U.S. Public Health Service, Cincinnati, Ohio.

264. Lovelock, J. E.   Anal. Chem. **33**, 162 (1961).

265. Lugg, G. A.   Anal. Chem. **41**, 1911 (1969).

266. Gisclard, J. B.   Ind. Eng. Chem. **15**, 582 (1943).

267. *International Critical Tables*, (New York: McGraw-Hill Book Company, Inc., 1929).

268. Lugg, G. A.   Anal. Chem. **40**, 1072 (1968).

269. Chen, N. H., and D. F. Othmer.   J. Chem. Eng. Data **7**, 37 (1962).

270. Nafikov, E. M., and A. G. Usmanov.   Inzh. Fiz. Zh. Akad. Nauk Belorussk. SSR **17**, 530 (1969).

271. Roberts, R. C.   *American Institute of Physics Handbook* (New York: McGraw-Hill Book Company, Inc., 1957).

272. Gilliland, E. R.   Ind. Eng. Chem. **26**, 681 (1934).

273. Treybal, R. E.   *Mass Transfer Operations* (New York: McGraw-Hill Book Company, Inc., 1955).

274. Lee, C. Y., and C. R. Wilke.   Ind. Eng. Chem. **46**, 238 (1954).

275. Brochure, Polyscience Corporation, Evanston, Illinois.

276. Linch, A. L., R. F. Stalzer, and D. T. Lefferts.   Am. Ind. Hyg. Assoc. J. **29**, 79 (1968).

277. Scaringelli, F. P., S. A. Frey, and B. E. Saltzman.   Am. Ind. Hyg. Assoc. J. **28**, 260 (1967).

278. O'Keeffe, A. E., and G. C. Ortman.   Anal. Chem. **38**, 760 (1966).

279. Stern, S. A., T. F. Sinclair, P. J. Gareis, N. P. Vahldieck, and P. H. Mohr.   Ind. Eng. Chem. **57**, 49)1965).

280. Meyer, J. A., C. Rogers, V. Stannett, and M. Szwarc.   Tappi **40**, 142 (1957).

281. Waack, R., N. H. Alex, H. L. Frisch, V. Stannett, and M. Szwarc. Ind. Eng. Chem. **47**, 2524 (1955).
282. Brubaker, D. W., and K. Kammermeyer. Ind. Eng. Chem. **45**, 1148 (1953).
283. Meares, P. J. Am. Chem. Soc. **76**, 3415 (1954).
284. Andrew, P., and R. Wood. Chem. Ind. (London) **1968**, 1936.
285. Bulletin No. 20–68, Metronics Associates, Inc., Palo Alto, California.
286. Stevens, R. K., A. E. O'Keeffe, and G. C. Ortman. Environ. Sci. Technol. **3**, 652 (1969).
287. Stern, S. A., J. T. Mullhaupt, and P. J. Gareis. Am. Inst. Chem. Eng. J. **15**, 64 (1969).
288. Li, N. N., and R. B. Long. Am. Inst. Chem. Eng. J. **15**, 73 (1969).
289. Saltzman, B. E., C. R. Feldmann, and A. E. O'Keeffe. Environ. Sci. Techol. **3**, 1275 (1969).
290. Rodes, C. E., H. F. Palmer, L. A. Elfers, and C. H. Norris. J. Air Pollution Control Assoc. **19**, 575 (1969).
291. Saltzman, B. E. J. Air Pollution Control Assoc. **18**, 326 (1968).
292. Heppel, L. A., P. A. Neal, T. L. Perrin, M. L. Orr, and V. T. Porterfield. J. Ind. Hyg. Tox. **26**, 8 (1944).
293. Weeks, M. H., G. C. Maxey, M. E. Sicks, and E. A. Greene. Am. Ind. Hyg. Assoc. J. **24**, 137 (1963).
294. Rinehart, W. E., R. C. Garbers, E. A. Greene, and R. M. Stoufer. Am. Ind. Hyg. Assoc. J. **19**, 80 (1958).
295. Stopps, G. J., and M. McLaughlin. Am. Ind. Hyg. Assoc. J. **28**, 43 (1967).
296. Campbell, E. E., M. F. Milligan, and H. M. Miller. Am. Ind. Hyg. Assoc. J. **20**, 138 (1959).
297. Amdur, M. O. Am. Ind. Hyg. Assoc. J. **22**, 1 (1961).
298. MacDonald, W. E., W. B. Deichmann, and E. Bernal. Am. Ind. Hyg. Assoc. J. **24**, 539 (1963).
299. Cohen, A. E. Am. Ind. Hyg. Assoc. J. **20**, 303 (1959).
300. Weeks, M. H., N. P. Musselman, P. P. Yevich, K, H. Jacobson, and F. W. Oberst. Am. Ind. Hyg. Assoc. J. **25**, 470 (1964).
301. Bolton, N. E., J. B. Johnson, W. H. McDermott, and V. T. Stack. Am. Ind. Hyg. Assoc. J. **20**, 32 (1959).
302. Hill, A. C., L. G. Transtrum, M. R. Pack, and A. Holloman. J. Air Pollution Control Assoc. **9**, 22 (1959).
303. Hill, A. C., L. G. Transtrum, M. R. Pack, and W. S. Winters. Am. Soc. Agron. J. **50**, 562 (1958).
304. Wilson, W. L., M. W. Campbell, L. D. Eddy, and W. H. Poppe. Am. Ind. Hyg. Assoc. J. **28**, 254 (1967).
305. Rinehart, W. E. Am. Ind. Hyg. Assoc. J. **21**, 389 (1960).
306. Rinehart, W. E., and T. Hatch. Am. Ind. Hyg. Assoc. J. **25**, 545 (1964).
307. Gelizunas, V. L. Anal. Chem. **41**, 1400 (1969).
308. Jahn, R. E. Analyst **80**, 700 (1955).
309. Kacy, H. W., and R. W. Cope. Am. Ind. Hyg. Assoc. J. **16**, 55 (1955).
310. Prager, M. J. Am. Ind. Hyg. Assoc. J. **27**, 272 (1966).

311. Marshall, E. K., and A. C. Kolls. J. Pharmacol. Exp. Therap. **12**, 385 (1918).

312. Sandage, C. *Tolerance Criteria for Continuous Inhalation Exposure to Toxic Material*, report No. ASD-61-519(I), U.S. Air Force, Wright-Patterson Air Force Base, Ohio (1961).

313. Rinehart, W. E. Am. Ind. Hyg. Assoc. J. **28**, 561 (1967).

314. Bryan, F. A., and V. Silis. Am. Ind. Hyg. Assoc. J. **21**, 423 (1960).

315. Private communication from N. Butterfield, Lawrence Radiation Laboratory, Livermore, California.

316. Hersch, P., C. J. Sambucetti, and R. Deuringer. Chim. Anal. (Paris) **46**, 31 (1964).

317. Pring, J. N., and G. M. Westrip. Nature **170**, 530 (1952).

318. Boer, H., and E. C. Kooyman. Anal. Chim. Acta **5**, 550 (1951).

319. Boer, H. Rec. Trav. Chim. **70**, 1020 (1951).

320. Boer, H. Rev. Trav. Chim. **67**, 217 (1948).

321. Noller, C. R. *Chemistry of Organic Compounds* (Philadelphia: W. B. Saunders Company, 1951).

322. Hersch, P., and R. Deuringer. J. Air Pollution Control Assoc. **13**, 538 (1963).

323. Shaw, J. T. Atomos. Environ. **1**, 81 (1967).

324. Page, J. A., and J. J. Lingane. Anal. Chim. Acta **16**, 175 (1957).

325. Waclawik, J. Chim. Anal. (Paris) **40**, 247 (1958).

326. Ludwick, J. D. Anal. Chem. **41**, 1907 (1969).

327. Singh, T., R. F. Sawyer, E. S. Starkman, and L. S. Caretto. J. Air Pollution Control Assoc. **18**, 102 (1968).

328. Hughes, J. G., and A. T. Jones. Am. Ind. Hyg. Assoc. J. **24**, 164 (1963).

329. Dechant, R., G. Sanders, and R. Graul. Am. Ind. Hyg. Assoc. J. **27**, 75 (1966).

330. Potter, L., and S. Duckworth. J. Air Pollution Control Assoc. **15**, 207 (1965).

331. Gill, W. E. Am. Ind. Hyg. Assoc. J. **21**, 87 (1960).

332. Stratman, H., and M. Buck. Intern. J. Air Water Pollution **10**, 313 (1966).

333. Palmes, E. D., N. Nelson, S. Laskin, and M. Kuschner. Am. Ind. Hyg. Assoc. J. **20**, 453 (1959).

334. Fieldner, A. C., G. G. Oberfell, M. C. Teague, and J. N. Lawrence. Ind. Eng. Chem. **11**, 519 (1919).

335. Williams, J. W., and C. D. Hurd, J. Org. Chem. **5**, 122 (1940).

336. Thienes, C. H., R. G. Skillen, A. Hoyt, and E. Bogen. Am. Ind. Hyg. Assoc. J. **26**, 255 (1965).

337. Deutsch, S. J. Air Pollution Control Assoc. **18**, 78 (1968).

338. Altshuller, A. P., and A. F. Wartburg. Intern. J. Air Water Pollution **4**, 70 (1961).

339. Pierce, L. B., K. Nishikawa, and N. O. Fansah. "Validation of Calibration Techniques," paper presented at the 8th Conference on Methods in Air Pollution and Industrial Hygiene Studies, Oakland, California, 1967.

340. Adams, D. F.   J. Air Pollution Control Assoc. 13, 88 (1963).
341. Horwood, J. H.   J. Air Pollution Control Assoc. 9, 42 (1959).
342. Brochure, Mast Development Company, Davenport, Iowa.
343. Regener, V. H.   Ozone Measuring Devices, report No. AFCRL-64-212, University of New Mexico, Albuquerque, New Mexico (1963).
344. Regener, V. H.   J. Geophys. Res. 69, 3795 (1964).
345. Hersch, P., and R. Deuringer.   Anal. Chem. 35, 897 (1963).
346. Brewer, A. W., and J. R. Milford.   Proc. Roy. Soc. (London, Ser. A. 256, 470 (1960).
347. Menser, H. A., and H. E. Heggestad.   Crop. Sci. 4, 103 (1964).
348. Kaye, S., and J. E. Koency.   Anal. Chem. 41, 1491 (1969).
349. Dardin, V. J.   J. Chem. Educ. 43, 439 (1966).
350. Kaye, S., and J. E. Koency.   Rev. Sci. Instr. 40, 505 (1969).
351. Richards, B. L., O. C. Taylor, and G. F. Edmunds.   J. Air Pollution Control Assoc. 18, 73 (1968).
352. Lunt, R. W.   "Mechanism of Ozone Formation in Electrical Discharges," in *Ozone Technology* (Washington, D.C.: American Chemical Society, 1956).
353. Hearn, A. G.   Proc. Phys. Soc. (London) 78, 932 (1961).
354. Hendricks, R. H., and L. B. Larson.   Am. Ind. Hyg. Assoc. J. 27, 80 (1966).
355. Jaffe, L. S.   Am. Ind. Hyg. Assoc. J. 28, 267 (1967).
356. Nash, T.   Atmos. Environ. 1, 679 (1967).
357. Larsen, L. B., and R. H. Hendricks.   Am. Ind. Hyg. Assoc. J. 30, 620 (1969).
358. Byers, D. H., and B. E. Saltaman.   Am. Ind. Hyg. Assoc. J. 19, 251 (1958).
359. Haagen-Smit, A. J., and M. F. Frunelle.   Intern. J. Air Water Pollution. 1, 51 (1958).
360. Egorov, M. S.   Z. Untersuch Lebensm. 56, 355 (1928).
361. Bovee, H. H., and R. J. Robinson.   Anal. Chem. 33, 1115 (1961).
362. Cherniack, I., and R. J. Brian.   J. Air Pollution Control Assoc. 15, 351 (1965).
363. Potter, L., and S. Duckworth.   J. Air Pollution Control Assoc. 15, 207 (1965).
364. Regener, V. H.   *The Preparation of Chemiluminescent Substance for the Measurement of Atmospheric Ozone*, repot No. AFCRL-66-246, University of New Mexico, Albuquerque, New Mexico (1966).
365. Nederbragt, G. W., A. Vander Horst, and J. Van Duijn.   Nature 206, 87 (1965).
366. Chleck, Z.   Intern. J. Appl. Radiation Isotopes 7, 141 (1959).
367. Hommel, C. O., D. Chleck, and F. J. Brousaides.   Nucleonics 19, 94 (1961).
368. Verhoek, F. H., and F. Daniels.   J. Am. Chem. Soc. 53, 1250 (1931).
369. Coon, E. D.   J. Am. Chem. Soc. 59, 1910 (1937).
370. Giauque, W. F., and J. D. Kemp.   J. Chem. Phys. 6, 40 (1938).

371. Atwood, K., and G. K. Rollefson.   J. Chem. Phys. 9, 506 (1941).
372. Adley, F. E., and C. P. Skillern.   Am. Ind. Hyg. Assoc. J. 19, 233 (1958).
373. Buck, M., and H. Stratmann. Staub 27, 11 (1967).
374. Kinosian, J. R., and B. R. Hubbard.   Am. Ind. Hyg. Assoc. J. 19, 453 (1958).
375. Moore, W. J.   *Physical Chemistry*, 2nd ed. (Englewood Cliffs, N. J.: Prentice-Hall, Inc., 1960).
376. Elkins, H. B.   J. Ind. Hyg. Toxicol 28, 37 (1946).
377. Wade, H. A., H. B. Elkins, and B. P. W. Ruotolo.   Arch. Ind. Hyg. Occup. Med. 1, 8 (1950).
378. Ayen, R. J., and T. Yonebayashi.   Atmos. Environ. 1, 307 (1967).
379. Serat, W. F., J. Kyono, and P. K. Mueller.   Atmos. Environ. 3, 303 (1969).
380. Rostenbach, R. E. and R. G. Kling.   J. Air Pollution Control Assoc. 12, 459 (1962).
381. Groth, R. H., and D. S. Calabro.   J. Air Pollution Control Assoc. 19, 884 (1969).
382. Rossano, A. T., and H. B. H. Cooper.   J. Air Pollution Control Assoc. 13, 518 (1963).
383. Shepherd, M., and S. Schuhmann.   J. Res. Natl. Bur. Std. 26, 357 (1941).
384. Nelson, G. O.   Rev. Sci. Instr. 41, 776 (1970).
385. Private communication from W. Va. Sandt, Lawrence Radiation Laboratory, Livermore, California.
386. Aldridge, W. J.   Analyst 69, 262 (1944).
387. Thompson, C. R., and J. O. Ivie.   Intern. J. Air Water Pollution 9, 799 (1965).
388. Bellack, E., and P. J. Schoubal.   Anal. Chem. 30, 2032 (1958).
389. Box, W. D.   Am. Ind. Hyg. Assoc. J. 24, 618 (1963).
390. Stephen, H., and T. Stephen.   *Solubilities of Inorganic and Organic Compounds* (New York: Macmillan Company, 1963).
391. Lange, N. A., Ed. *Handbook of Chemistry*, 10th ed. rev. (New York: McGraw-Hill Book Company, Inc., 1967).
392. Harris, F. E., and L. K. Nash.   Anal. Chem. 23, 736 (1951).
393. Henley, E. J., and H. Bieber.   Chemical Engineering Calculations (New York: McGraw-Hill Book Company, Inc., 1959).
394. Zimmerman, O. T., and I. Lavine.   *Psychrometric Tables and Charts*, 2nd ed. (Dover, N. H.: Industrial Research Service, Inc., 1964).
395. Hollander, L. E., D. S. Mills, and T. A. Perls.   ISA J. 7, 50 (1960).
396. Cole, K. M. and J. A. Reger.   Instr. Control Systems 43, 77 (1970).
397. Compt. Rend. Conf. Union Intern. Chim. Pure Appl. 23rd 1965, 177.
398. Brochure, Electrofilm, Inc., North Hollywood, Calif.
399. Lodge, J. P. and H. A. Bravo, Anal Chem. 36, 671 (1964).

Subject Index

243

This book was typeset at Allied Type-
setting, Ann Arbor, Michigan, and printed and bound by Litho Crafters, Inc.,
Ann Arbor, Michigan.